THE HEMINGWAY MANUSCRIPTS

AN INVENTORY

The
HEMINGWAY
Manuscripts
An Inventory

Philip Young
and
Charles W. Mann

The Pennsylvania State University Press
University Park and London

Standard Book Number 271–00080–5
Library of Congress Catalog Card Number 68–8189
The Pennsylvania State University Press, University Park 16802
The Pennsylvania State University Press, Ltd., London W.1
Text © 1969 by Philip Young and Charles W. Mann. All rights reserved.
Photographic material © 1969 by Mary Hemingway. All rights reserved.
Printed in the United States of America
Designed by Glenn Ruby

Publisher's note: *The Hemingway Manuscripts: An Inventory*
is also published in a separate, limited edition of 300 numbered copies.

CONTENTS

PREFACE

The great bulk of the surviving manuscripts of Ernest Hemingway are in the possession of Mrs. Hemingway, sole executrix of his estate, until such time as they may be suitably deposited and arranged for examination by scholars in years to come. This inventory of her husband's literary estate was originally prepared for her. But the fact of its more general interest was clear to its compilers, and she consented to its publication.

It should be made clear, first off, that this publication pretends to be no more than what it says: an "inventory" ("an itemized list of current assets: as . . . the property of an individual or estate; a list of goods on hand"), and not the much more elaborate catalogue ("a complete enumeration of items . . . with descriptive details") that should be made when the papers have reached their permanent repository.

Such an interim report, however, should at least silence some rumors and ill-founded speculation. One headline that has seen print, for example, reads "Up to 50,000 Hemingway Manuscript Pages Remain Unpublished," and nicely epitomizes how far off some of the guesswork has been. No exact count of all sheets, scraps, and jottings was made in the present undertaking, but a careful estimate is that there are somewhat in excess of 19,500 pages of manuscript in the holdings, of which more than 3,000 pages are unpublished. (The word "manuscript" is used here as a compendium term to cover holograph, typescript, re-

typescript, carbon, and proof—whether pristine, or lightly or heavily edited by the author; by "page" is meant everything from a full sheet of writing or print, to a poem pencilled inside the torn-off cover of a book, to a few words occupying an entire leaf, 8½″ x 11″.) Nor was any attempt made to supply dates for manuscripts except where the author himself occasionally did so; at times it appeared that over the decades the condition of the paper on which he wrote—or his typing habits—changed as much as his calligraphy.

Another rumor that will hopefully be stilled here is that the executrix has taken no care of the estate—has even destroyed literary remains. To the contrary, in some cases manuscripts had been informally stored in such unqualified places as the back room of a Key West saloon, Castro's Cuba, the home in Ketchum, Idaho, and elsewhere, and were rescued by Mrs. Hemingway from these locations.

Hemingway kept nearly everything from note to novel, from the 1919 Chicago days before the Paris apprenticeship had begun to the bitter end. Except for work actually in progress, however, he took little or no care of what he saved. Thus paper clips and common pins have rusted completely through some musty pages where the author stuck them long ago; holes clean through buried texts testify how worms in private tried an ill-preserved virginity; tiny teeth marks record the visit of mice which in Key West also left their skeletons. Yet for all their efforts, the salt air, rodents, and various insects accomplished less than might be expected: by and large the manuscripts are in good condition. When brought together by Mrs. Hemingway and locked in several enormous safe-deposit boxes in the vault of a New York bank, or wrapped and stored in the library or in closets of her New York apartment en route to the bank, the manuscripts received meticulous care. This inventory was compiled in both places, and so far as is known not even the torn corner of a sheet has been lost, discarded, or appreciably damaged since the papers were assembled.

One question that publication of this volume will quicken rather than quiet, however, concerns which of all the unpublished pages entered here may ultimately see print. The question is overriding but as of now premature: final decisions have simply not been made. All this is up to Mary Hemingway—in consultation with Charles Scribner's Sons, the author's publishers since 1926, and probably others. But decision has been reached regarding the principles of posthumous publication. First, it is not contemplated that anything that would risk reduction of the author's stature will appear; second, the ground rules have it that cuts may be made in original or unrevised (hence "unfinished") material, but nothing is to be added to what Hemingway himself wrote.

To be sure, this position has already been challenged in a letter to the *Times:* "no one man, or committee, or publisher has the right to deny a reading audience a look at the whole writer—especially Hemingway. Warts and all . . ." Many people may feel this way, especially scholars, but scholars will have access to these materials, which is very different from having them printed. And it does not follow that everything written by a man ought to be published just because he was an important writer. As the contemporary

ix

novelist John Barth—himself a destroyer, not a keeper
—has written in this connection,

> death may not give enough advance notice for
> putting one's literary affairs in order. . . . If
> I'm killed in a car crash on the way home
> tonight, $\frac{9}{10}$ of the papers I'll leave behind will
> be ones I'd've destroyed if I'd known. . . . The
> finished draft is all that matters, and to say
> that the author owes us more, when in fact it's
> we who are in his debt for what he's given us,
> is contemptible.

Further, as already observed, many of Hemingway's
pages were simply not at hand during the last months
of his life had he wanted to rid himself of them.

On the other hand, his retention of so much manuscript, and his references to his unpublished work as
"life insurance," make up part of the evidence that
not all he planned to print was issued during his life-
time. *A Moveable Feast* was not, and there is reason to
hope for more in the future—two or three more short
stories about Nick Adams, for instance, and maybe all
or part of a long untitled work here called the "Sea
Novel." It might also be worth noting that more than
once the author announced that he intended to bring
out a book of poems. Other possibilities are entered
on this itemized list.

But it is likely that those who are sufficiently inter-
ested in Hemingway to examine this inventory have
enough scholar, student, or reliquarian in them to want
to learn not just of the existence of new or withheld
material, but also of early drafts of now-famous works,
and what names such works as *The Sun Also Rises,*

"The Killers," and "The Snows of Kilimanjaro" originally bore. So the compilers were taken not only with
discovery of unknown writing, but also with well-
known work, the cruder the version the more arrest-
ing. As good as anything was contact with quite a bit of
cheap and well-aged paper covered by the hand of an
obscure novice during the halcyon days in Paris. This
was when, as he wrote much later in the "Sea Novel,"
"I would feel like I was making the whole world."

University Park
March, 1969

ACKNOWLEDGMENTS

We express our gratitude to the various individuals and offices that helped make this Inventory possible. We are indebted to The Pennsylvania State University's English Department, and to its Pattee Library, for the time during which we were released from ordinary responsibilities to do this work, and to its Liberal Arts Research Office and its Institute for the Arts and Humanistic Studies for uncluttered financial support. We also cite the expert cooperation of Carlos Baker, Hemingway's authorized biographer, and Audre Hanneman, his bibliographer, and record our obligation to Mary Hemingway, his widow, and Charles Scribner's Sons, his publishers, for permission to report on or reproduce such material as appears here for the first time. We are grateful to David Morrell for preparing the index and helping with proof. Last and most we thank Mrs. Hemingway for the cheerful, unflagging hospitality, generosity, and thoughtfulness that made a memorable undertaking even more rewarding.

P.Y.
C.W.M.

BOOKS

1 *ACROSS THE RIVER AND INTO THE TREES*

[A] Typescript, original, few pencil corrections, 370 pages. Pagination 1–369. Insert at page 63. Pages 239 to the end originally numbered 1–131, renumbered in pencil, not by EH. (Manuscript dog-eared.)

Note by Mary Hemingway (MH): "First copy of first typed mans. of 'Across the River and into the Trees,' with corrections in EH handwriting and also by Gigi Viertel, now dead. Corrections were made in the late fall of 1949 aboard *Île de France* and at Ritz Hotel, Paris. M."

[B] Typescript and manuscript in pencil, corrections in ink and pencil. Pagination 1–349. Sections clipped together and crushed into a yellow typing-paper box. Word counts and dates all over both halves of box, inside and out, and on the sides. Dated March, 1949. Pages 197–235 in pencil.

[C] Typescript, carbon, uncorrected. 283 pages.

[D] Typescript, original and carbon. Pencil corrections, not by EH. Pagination 1–136. First page, original, has corrections by EH in ink.

[E] Galley proofs, 87 galleys. Uncorrected set.

[F] Two notebooks, unruled, numbered one and two, containing drafts and studies for different parts of the novel as follows:

[i] "No. 1" "This is what the Colonel thinks about when the duck flight slows up. . . ." Typescript, seven pages, ink corrections.

[ii] "Next to Last Chapter—Second Take." Manuscript in pencil. Six pages. Pagination 1–6.

[iii] "To follow previously labeled next to last chapter —4th take." Manuscript in pencil, sparse corrections, 50 pages. Pagination 1–49, 49 bis ("a second time").

[iv] "Last Chapter" starts on page 47.

[v] "No 2" "Last Chapter—(continued)" Manuscript in pencil, sparse corrections, 12 pages. Pagination 50–61.

[G] Manuscript in pencil, insert to page 63, two pages.

[H] Typescript, insert to page 63.

[I] Typescript, carbon, corrections in ink and pencil, interlinear and marginal. Pagination 137–226. Manuscript in ink after page 216.

[J] Typescript, triple-spaced, corrected in ink. Pagination 350–81. On verso of Finca Vigía letterhead.

[K] Typescript, ink corrections. Pagination 350–71. Also two corrected carbons.

[L] Typescript draft of "What the Colonel thinks about when the duck flight slows up . . ." Ink and pencil corrections. Note by EH: "(Write this 2/3/50 in pencil)."

[M] Typescript, corrections, not all in hand of EH. Pagination 1–28. Draft for next to last chapter. Also two other corrected carbons present.

[N] Typescript, carbon, few corrections in ink and pencil, not by EH. 47 pages. Pagination 350–71.

[O] Manuscript notes in ink, Finca Vigía letterhead, on paging and chapter order. One page.

[P] Manuscript in pencil of word counts, various dates, earliest July 28, 1949, latest August 6, 1951. One page.

[Q] Manuscript of passage in Spanish, French, and Italian, not in EH hand. One page.

[R] Manuscript of "Marcelle's notes for Mr. Hemingway 19 Dec 1949." One page. Corrections for French phrases.

[S] Maurice Rostand, *Île de France Poème,* printed on the *Île de France.* Paper wrapper. Plaquette no. 299 of

500. Note in pencil on back: "See if can work in poem when Colonel is on bed thinking how it was."

[T] Manuscript in ink, some pencil corrections, 15 pages, some on stationery of Hotel Ritz. Pagination 1–15. Note: "3rd take—next to last chapt. 30/11/49."

2 ["AFRICAN BOOK"] *   (*unpublished*)

[A] Typescript in manila folders. Pagination 1–850. In manuscript from page 698 to end. Two pages paginated 216. Page 342 torn in half. 271–79 missing, 790–99 missing. Autobiographical account of duties as volunteer ranger at the Masai game preserve at foot of Mt. Kilimanjaro in late 1953. Manuscript dated 1955. Unfinished.

[B] Folder of manuscript notes in pencil. Background material for above. Six pages. Pagination 1–6.

---

* Titles in brackets are either Hemingway's working titles or ones supplied by the compilers.

3 *THE DANGEROUS SUMMER*

[A] Manuscript in ink, pages folded and wrinkled, few corrections in ink and pencil. Pagination 1–332, 845–928, five-page insert after page 928. Top sheet torn in fragments.

[B] Manuscript in ink, corrections interlinear and marginal. Opens with ten page insert to page 332. Pagination 1–10, 333–638.

[C] Manuscript in ink, very few corrections. Pagination 639–844. Some inserts and additions stapled to various pages. Paging renumbered throughout, changing from 539 to 639 and so on until the end.

[D] Typescript, original. Very few corrections in pencil and ink. Pagination 1–688.

[E] Typescript, carbon, triple-spaced, few corrections in ink and pencil. Pagination 1–688. Some sections published in *Life,* Sept. 5, 12, 19, 1960; otherwise unpublished.

4 *DEATH IN THE AFTERNOON*

[A] Typescript and manuscript pages intermingled. Many inserts in holograph. Pagination 1–213. Page 16 skipped in numbering, pages 31 and 81 missing.

[B] "Absolutely necessary photographs." Manuscript list in ink, five pages. Pagination 1–5.

[C] "Appendix A." Manuscript in ink, corrected. Pagination 1–9. Also typescript, corrected. Five pages. Pagination 1–5. Repaginated in pencil, 96–100.

[D] "Appendix D. A Short Estimate of the American, Sidney Franklin, as a matador." Typescript, corrected in pencil, five pages. Pagination 1–5.

[E] Manuscript page of word counts for Appendices and Glossary.

[F] "The Natural History of the Dead." Typescript, assorted drafts, 33 pages, pencil and ink corrections, various pagings. Pagination 110A–C, insert, 110D–L, 111, 122A, 46, 46 bis, 46 (2), 144A–I, 137A–C, three pages ink insert of "Old Lady Conversation." One loose page in pencil.

[G] "An Explanatory Glossary." Manuscript in pencil and ink, corrections interlinear and marginal. Pagination 1–32, 33 bis, 33–53, 53–65, 67–129 [130]. Page 66 missing.

[H] Typescript fragment of Glossary, corrections in pencil and ink. Pagination 16–95.

[I] "New Chapter Cogidas." Manuscript in pencil, corrections, six pages. Pagination 1–6.

[J] "Death of Bullfighters." Manuscript in ink, corrections, eight pages. Pagination 1–8. Draft of the same.

[K] "Last Chapter." Manuscript in ink, corrections, 45 pages. Pagination 1–7, [two-page insert], 8–42.

[L] Typescript, pencil corrections. Pagination 110G–J, 111–22, 122A–B, 123–32, 132A–B, 133–37, 137A–D, 144, 144A–C, 145–53, 153A, 154–93.

[M] Typescript and photostat pages, ink corrections. Pagination 52–72, seven pages of unpaginated photostat, 80–233. Pages 52–62 in photostat.

[N] Picture Captions. Manuscript in pencil, corrections interlinear and marginal. 72 pages. Pagination 1–69, 69, 69 (1–2), 70. With envelope dated April 12, 1932.

[O] Manuscript in pencil, corrections, 16 pages. Pagination 85–100. Blank page after page 87. Wormed.

[P] Package of heavily corrected galleys, including main text, text for photographs, and Appendices. Many inserts, pencil and typescript, inserted, pinned, stapled, clipped, pasted, folded in, or added marginally. Wormed, much handled.

[Q] Complete set of galleys of book-proper, uncorrected, last two an ending—on writers and painters working at home or abroad—not included in work as published. Glossary through "B" only, no Appendix. KW *

[R] Typescript, carbon, 218 pages. Pagination 1–218. Complete book-proper with deleted ending but no Glossary or Appendix. KW

[S] Page proofs, uncorrected. Paginated 97–278, 409–517. KW

[T] Page proofs. Paginated 1–370 only. KW

[U] Miscellaneous typescripts, carbon, of sections of the work. KW

5 *A FAREWELL TO ARMS*

[A] Manuscript, 662 pages. Working draft, heavily revised. Currently on deposit at Harvard University.

---

* In memory of the years during which her husband lived and wrote in Key West, Florida, Mrs. Hemingway gave manuscripts here and below labeled KW to the Monroe County Public Library.

[B] Typescript, original, few corrections in ink and pencil. Pagination 1–322. Late draft.

[C] Typescript, carbon, sparse corrections in ink and pencil, 322 pages. Pagination 1–322. Setting copy. Top sheet brown and stained.

[D] *Along with Youth a Novel* June 15, 1925." Pencil manuscript in notebook, 26 pages, and part of another. Opens "The Polish officers . . ." Set on the *Chicago* crossing to France, in late May, 1918. Discarded opening to *A Farewell to Arms*. Main character called "Nick." Also manuscript notes in ink on correspondence, and manuscripts sent out and returned.

[E] Manuscript in pencil, ten pages. Pagination 489, 202–9. Drafts for a love scene.

[F] Manuscript in pencil, three pages. Draft for ending. Baby, a boy, alive.

[G] "It was a hot night. . . ." Manuscript in ink, two pages torn from a notebook. Polish officers on shipboard, the *Chicago,* May 1918. Another draft for aborted opening to *A Farewell to Arms.*

[H] Foul galleys for *Scribner's Magazine* appearance dated Feb. 18, Mar. 5, Mar. 15, Mar. 25, Apr. 15, Apr. 22, 1929, with letter from Maxwell Perkins, June 1, 1929. Corrections in galleys both marginal and interlinear by EH. Different versions of ending attached. Note: "All through galleys change Greppi to Greffi EH."

[I] 79 galleys, first dated May 2, 1929. Pencil corrections interlinear and marginal by EH. Query about "bedpan" on 4 Gal 23 by Maxwell Perkins, answered by EH.

[J] Two galleys, "Gal 19—Farewell VI—61692," dated "June 4, 1929," marked "Hold October." Typescript, carbon, pinned to second galley with four more endings to the novel.

[K] 87 galleys, dated July 19, 1929. Pencil corrections by EH.

6 *THE FIFTH COLUMN*

[A] Typescript and manuscript in ink and pencil intermingled. Badly damp-stained, rust-marked, and stained throughout by a waxy, brown substance. Many pages adhering.

[B] Fragment, in wrapper, badly chewed and damp-stained. Begins with Scene Six. 35 pages, note at beginning, half page at end. Pagination 2–10, 10A, 11–30, 41–43, 55–56, half page at end unnumbered. Note to typist, bottom page 18.

[C] Typescript, pencil corrections and insert. "Copyrighted—1938 Property of Joseph Losey 1430 Broadway New York City." Production script.

7 *THE FIFTH COLUMN AND THE FIRST FORTY-NINE STORIES*

Typescript, carbon. Pencil corrections, badly worn, 60 pages. Pagination 634–693/4 supplied by printer, lower right hand corner. Fragment of setting copy including:

[i] "The Short Happy Life of Francis Macomber" Typescript, carbon. Pagination 1–33. Repaginated 634–72. Very crumbly brown paper, some corners gone.

[ii] "The Capital of the World" Typescript, carbon. Pagination 1–20. Repaginated 673–693/4.

[iii] Galley for Preface. Pencil and ink corrections interlinear and marginal. Dated Aug. 24, 1938 and Sept. 1, 1938.

[iv] Typescript of Preface. KW

8 *FOR WHOM THE BELL TOLLS*

[A] Manuscript and typescript, 1,160 pages, all but approximately 350 pages in holograph. Complete working draft, heavily revised. Chapter 32 in two slightly variant versions. Currently on deposit at Harvard University.

[B] Galley proofs, 122 pages, through Chapter 40. Ink and pencil corrections, interlinear and marginal; some additions.

[C] Typescript, two pages. Pencil and ink corrections. Additions to galley 21 and to galley 22.

9 ["GARDEN OF EDEN"]   (*unpublished*)

[A] Manuscript arranged in folders and an envelope by MH with descriptive notes and chapter numbers in each folder. Notes by EH: "First 4 chapters Le Grau du Roi [early title] David Bourne." Other notes by EH: "Original mss. (only copy) Book two with instructions and notes." "Sept. 20, 58. Final Chapter written May '58 when thought something might happen." Other notes. Autobiographically-based fiction, set in Twenties, concerning two pairs of lovers: David and Catherine at Le-Grau-du-Roi, Nick (Sheldon) and Barbara in Paris.

14

[B] Envelope contains mixed typescript and manuscript in pencil, 155 pages. Pagination scrambled, frequent inserts and additions. Also notes and rough drafts present. Comprises roughly Chapters 1–4, and a draft for a possible finishing chapter, with a note: "Provisional ending written when thought something might happen before book could be finished. EH"

[C] Typescript, original, triple-spaced; pencil corrections not in hand of EH. Includes Book II, Book III, Chapters 1–8, 32–39, 40–46, and provisional ending.

[D] Typescript, carbon, uncorrected. Chapters 32–46.

[E] Typescript, carbon, uncorrected, 28 chapters. No Chapter 26.

[F] Photocopy of original typescript. Pencil notes by EH on top: "Nick at Hendaye, Andy at Madrid, David's African Background."

[G] Discarded manuscript drafts in pencil for Chapters 24, 25, and scattered pages.

[H] Notes for "Garden of Eden." Photocopy, three pages.

10 *GREEN HILLS OF AFRICA*

[A] Typescript, mixed original and carbon. Interlinear and marginal corrections in ink and pencil, 231 pages. Pagination [i–iv], 2–48, 132–323.

[B] Typescript, original, ink and pencil corrections, 99 pages. Pagination 1–98. Insert after page 48 numbered 48A. Slips pasted on pages 27 and 48A. (Setting copy?)

[C] Fragments of typescript, pencil corrections, 97 pages. Pagination 224A–323. Pages 303–6 on one page. Page 323, top left hand margin torn away affecting four lines of text. Setting copy? In envelope addressed to "Mr. Ernest Hemingway Yacht 'Pilar' Bimini British West Indies" from Big Horn, Wyo. July 16, 1935.

[D] Galley proofs, sparse corrections. KW

[E] "It is still permitted to love a new country. . . ." About a Kudu bull. Manuscript in pencil, three pages.

[F] "For God's sake Abdullah. . . ." Manuscript in pencil, one sentence only.

11   [*in our time*] (Paris)

[A] Typescript, original and carbons heavily corrected in type and pencil, 51 pages. Various pagings and sizes.

[B] "Maera was awake in his bed. . . ." Manuscript, two pages. Pagination 1–3, page 1 recto and verso.

[C] "Personal." Manuscript in pencil, two pages folded. "One hot evening in Milan they carried me up onto the roof. . . ." Very eary draft for "Chapter 10," later called "A Very Short Story."

[D] "The horse galloped across the ring leaving a trail of blood. . . ." Manuscript in pencil on a letter dated 15 June 1925. Folded into a quarto paged 1–4, and continued on verso as page five. Draft of "Chapter 12," apparently.

[E] "Unwritten Stories." Typescript, one page, pencil corrections. Two drafts for *in our time*. One on bull fighting, the other for "Everybody was drunk. . . ." "Chapter 1."

12 *IN OUR TIME* (New York)

Typescript, carbon. Revised and corrected in ink, pencil, and typescript. Pagination 1–57, 69–157. Sheets from Paris *in our time* included. Other stories supplied from sheets of *Three Stories and Ten Poems,* Dijon, 1923, and magazine appearances, e.g. "Indian Camp." Title for "Soldier's Home" (p. 57) present but not the story.

13 ["JIMMY BREEN"]   (*unpublished*)

[A] Manuscript in pencil, corrections. Chapters 1–20 of uncompleted novel. Various drafts and starts intermixed. Alternate title lined out: *A New Slain Knight A Novel.* (Title from "Twa Corbies.") Opens "Chapter One. In which goodbye is said to the Old Places in the First Person." About "Jimmy Breen," a boy, his father, and an older friend. To Chicago by train, then to New York, en route to Paris where his mother lives. Father is a revolutionist.

[B] "Ahead of them sat two other men. . . ." Manuscript in pencil, one page. Pagination 10. Boy and father on a train, man in handcuffs.

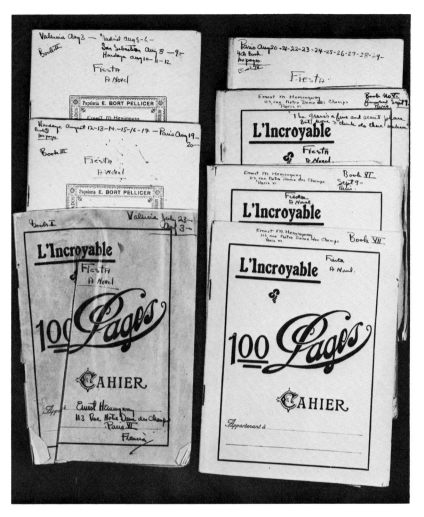

The "Fiesta notebooks," early draft of *The Sun Also Rises*.
Note varying signatures, and the misquotation from Marvell.

The Sun Also Rises

A Novel

By Ernest Hemingway

You are all a lost generation —
Gertrude Stein in conversation.

> Vanity of vanities, saith the Preacher,
> vanity of vanities; all is vanity ....
> One generation passeth away, and another
> generation cometh; but the earth abideth
> for ever .... The sun also ariseth, and
> the sun goeth down, and hasteth to the
> place where he arose ... The wind
> goeth toward the south, and turneth about
> unto the north; it whirleth about
> continually, and the wind returneth again
> according to his circuits ... All the
> rivers run into the sea; yet the sea
> is not full; unto the place from whence
> the rivers come, thither they return again.

Ecclesiastes.

The Stein remark on title page of *The Sun Also Rises* typescript entered in pencil; second epigraph longer than version published. Showing through sheet is unfamiliar first page of novel ("This is a novel about a lady. . . ."), discarded after printing in galleys.

together."

Ahead was a mounted policeman in Khaki. * directing traffic. The car slowed suddenly pressing Duff closer against me . "Yes," I said. "It's nice as hell to think so."

The End.

Paris - Sept. 21 - 1925

"Isn't it nice to think so"

Last page of notebook draft of *The Sun Also Rises,* with Brett (Ashley) appearing as Duff (Twysden), her real name. Passage incomplete; neither version of last line final.

Summer People.

Halfway down the gravel road ~~that~~ from Hortons Bay, the town, to the lake there was a spring. The water came up ~~out~~ ~~=~~ in a tile sunk beside the road, lipping over the cracked edge of the tile and flowing away through the ~~the~~ close growing ~~In the dark~~ ~~(Nick Wemedge)~~ ~~(Allan)~~ ~~Nick~~ mint into the swamp. ~~Nick~~ ~~=~~ put ~~your~~ his arm down into the spring ~~but~~ could not hold it there because of the cold, ~~although~~ ~~you could feel~~

He felt the featherings of the sand spouting up from the spring cones at the

Probably first "Nick Adams story," the author vacillating on protagonist's first name. Deleted names read Nick, Wemedge—eventually a nickname—and Allan.

The ~~Matadors~~
Killers

Madrid — May 1926
Ernest Hemingway

The door of Henry's lunch room opened and two men came in. They sat down at the counter.

"What's yours?" George asked them.

"I don't know," one of the men said. "What do you want to eat, Al."

"I don't know," said Al. "I don't know what I want to eat."

Outside it was getting dark. The streetlight came on outside the window. The two men at the counter read the menu. At the other end of the counter Nick Adams watched them. He had been talking to George when they came in.

"I'll have a roast pork tenderloin with apple sauce and mashed potato," the first man said.

"It isn't ready yet."

"What the hell do you put it on the card for ~~xxxx~~?"

"That's the dinner," George explained. "You can get that at six o'clock."

"What time is it now?"

George looked at the clock on the wall ~~behind xxxxx~~ ~~blackx~~ behind the counter.

"It's five o'clock."

"The clock says twenty minutes past five," the second man said.

"It's twenty minutes fast."

"Oh to hell with the clock," the first man said.

"What have you got to eat?"

"I can give you any kind of sandwiches," George said. "You can have ham and eggs, bacon and eggs, liver and

For Uncle Gus! written between 215 and 8[?] pm

Originally "The Matadors," first page of "The Killers" was published as typed here but for five accidentals, change of one word, and deletion of one sentence ("What time is it now?"). Marginalia read "Madrid—May 1926 Ernest Hemingway" and "For Uncle Gus [Pfeiffer]! Written between 215 and 8[?] pm."

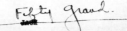

Fifty grand.

(A Story)

~~fxxxyxxix~~ (now over the)

Up at the Garden one time somebody says to
Jack ,"Say Jack how did you happen to beat Leonard anyway ?"
and Jack says ,"Well , he says , you/Benny's an awful smart
boxer . All the time he's in there he's thinking and all the
time he's thinking I was hitting him ."

        That got a big laugh and somebody ,Soldier
Bartfield I think , says ,"You're quite a kidder aint you
Jack?"

    "Yes," says Jack."I'm quite a kidder ."

    " How did you beat Kid Lewis ?" Asked Soldier .

    " That kike ," Jack says .

    " Benny's a kike too ," Soldier says .

    " No he's not ," Jack said ."Benny's no kike .Beny's
a Jewish boy . ~~He's a d amn fine fighter .~~"

    "He's an actor now ," somebody said .

    " Corbett got to be an actor too ," somebody else said .
There was a laugh in that too if you could find it .

    "Benny's not that way ,"Harry Collins said .

    " Well " says Jack ."I'm not an actor anyway ."

    " No you're just a big hearted kidder ," Soldier
says .

    "You make a lot of funny cracks ," Jack says .

    "It's just my happy nature ," Soldier says ."When
(when) I'm/ around with a lot of you big hearted spenders. I~~ just~~
~~have to talk .~~

    " All right ," Jack says ," Come one . I'll buy
you the drink ."

Opening of "Fifty Grand" discarded by author because, as he
explained later in an unpublished essay, Fitzgerald objected
that the opening paragraph, a "lovely revelation of the meta-
physics of boxing," was "an old chestnut because he had heard
it once, and only once from a friend. . . ." (Thus Hemingway
"realized how dangerous that attractive virtue humility can
be.") Another two and one-fourth pages rejected without ex-
planation. The title was originally "Jack" (Brennan, in life Jack
Britton). On upper right corner author writes "1st 3 pages
of story mutilated by Scott Fitzgerald with [?] his"—the rest
illegible. Corner has been torn off (by author?), replaced by
editors.

14 *MEN WITHOUT WOMEN*

"Foundry set" of proofs dated Sept. 26, 1927.

15 [*A MOVEABLE FEAST*]
(posthumously published)

[A] Manuscript in pencil, some pages typescript. Pencil corrections, interlinear and marginal; 169 pages, one blank. Thirteen chapters, separately paged. Headnote for Fitzgerald section considerably older than rest of manuscript.

[B] Typescript, chapters stapled together. Chapters 1, 3, original. Chapters 2, 4–19, carbon. Notes and corrections in MH hand. Note by EH at head of Chapter 13: "This is too dangerous and libelous to publish (as explained in letter to Charlie Scribner)." Rewritten Chapters 5 and 6 loosely inserted after Chapter 5. Labeled in hand of MH: "Rewritten and Revised Chaps. 5 and 6."

[C] Manuscript, pencil and typescript. With carbon of MH cover letter to Harry [Brague], July 27, 1963: "Paris book as revised by Papa from the first draft. This is the only corrected copy." Many drafts, inserts, corrections, etc.

[D] Typescript, carbon, uncorrected. Late draft. In envelope with manuscript notes by EH on outside.

[E] Manuscript in pencil, eight pages. Pagination 1–8. First six sheets dated April 1, the seventh, April 2, the eighth, April 3. Note by MH on last sheet: "This part about Evan Shipman, now dead, happened in Cuba in 1956 or 1957, M.H." Unpublished final chapter for *A Moveable Feast.*

[F] "Possible finishing chapter—M.H." Seven pages. Dated "April 1" in upper right hand corner of first sheet. Pages 1–6, dated April 2; page 7 dated April 3.

[G] "Then you remember Evan the last time in Cuba when he came over with the pancreas cancer." Manuscript in pencil, corrected, four sheets. Pagination 1–3, 6. Draft for unused final chapter. Also photocopy present.

[H] Drafts for Preface. Manuscript in ink and pencil, two pages.

[I] "Mike Ward was . . ." Manuscript in pencil, eight pages. Scattered unused sheets for Paris book.

[J] "Larry Gains was a tall, long muscled negro. . . ." "Paris Book" section, unused. Manuscript in pencil and typescript. Nine pages. Two drafts.

[K] "(For Book) Paris" Manuscript in pencil, one page. On weather.

16 *THE OLD MAN AND THE SEA*

[A] Typescript, original, triple-spaced, double-spaced between words, pencil corrections, 119 pages, two blank. Pagination 1–41, 43–69, 65–112. Blank pages between pages 97–98, 102–3; last page blank.

[B] Typescript, corrections in ink. "First typescript" in hand of MH, 100 pages. Pagination 1–101, page 42 renumbered 41/42.

[C] Both above in paper box labeled in MH hand "Mss —and 1st typescript." On bottom half of box is penciled note by EH: "There's more than that. *The Old and the Young*. A novel by Ernest Hemingway (this is one of the three books of the first volume of a three volume novel the sea, the air and the land.)"

17 "SEA NOVEL"   (*unpublished*)

In three books of approximately 17, 4, and 21 chapters.

[A] "Book One Chapter One."

[i] Manuscript in pencil, occasional page in typescript, 445 pages. Pagination 1, insert, 2, 6 page insert, 3–6, 6–40, 4 page insert, 41, 41–65, 22 page

insert, 66–71, 2 page insert, 94, 6 page insert, 95–102, insert, 103–6, 2 page insert, 107–28, insert, 129–72, 173 bis, 173, 173–257, blank, 258–68, 270–91, 289, 3 page insert, 290–99, insert, 300–26, insert, 327–79. Page 269 skipped in numbering, 307 badly torn. Seven pages of scraps and notes inserted after 291. In box labeled by EH "Rewritten Mss. March 26, 1947." (Probably does not refer to present contents.)

[ii] Manuscript in pencil, 315 pages. Pagination 380–406, blank, 407–73, 473 bis, 474–526, 524–41, insert, 542–50, 550–51, 551–94, 6 page insert, 595–96, 2 page insert, 597, 2 page insert, 598–673, 675–77, blank, 678–80, 841–42. Page 388 badly torn and mended and copied in unknown hand. Page 390 torn and mended, 674 missing, 680 headed "Book Two Chapter One."

[B] "Sea Novel Book Two." Chapters 1–3, 258 pages, manuscript in pencil. Pagination 680–718, 2 page insert, 719–36, insert, 737, 2 page insert, 738, insert, 739–53, 4 page insert, 762–78, 778–826, insert, 827–56, insert, 857–60, 2 page insert, 861–907. Sheet of word counts inserted after 778.

[C] "Book Two." Typescripts, original and carbon, few corrections in unknown hand. Chapters 1–4.

[D] "Part One The Island and the Stream." Chapters 1–17, 482 pages, typescript and manuscript in pencil. Pagination 1–3, 3–15, 2 page insert, 16–25, 25, 26–28, 28a and b, 29–32, 34–93, 95–185, 185 (continued)–328, 330–71, 373–441, 7 page insert, 442–57,

457–73. Pages 33, 94, 329, 372 skipped in numbering. Sheet of word counts inserted after 441. Various dates from May 1, 1951—August 6, 1951. On page 2, note by EH "Page 2 (of re-write). (Starting re-writing page 2 of First Part of mss.)" Draft greatly expanded from typescript in manuscript, many pages renumbered, sometimes twice. Notes by EH on changes of names and point of view. Many pages marked "R.W.P.I." (rewrite part one).

[E] "Part One The Island and the Stream." Typescripts, originals and three carbons, very few corrections in pencil.

[F] Manuscript and typescript, extensive pencil correction, 79 pages. Pagination 2–8, "16th page R.W.P.I.," 9–32, 33, 32–76.

[G] "The Sea (Main Book Two) Section One." Typescript, pencil corrections, 82 pages. In envelope with note by EH "The Sea—Main Book Two Part One."

[H] "The Sea—Main Book Two continued. EH." Manuscript and typescript, 76 pages. Pagination 74–100, 100–03, blank, 104–45, 3 page insert.

[I] "The Sea Main Book Two." Typescript, triple-spaced, corrected. Chapters 1–20, 226 pages. Pagination 1–64, 60–83, 83 bis, 84–109, 109 bis, 110–27, 127, 128–219. Pages 60–69 renumbered from 55–63, 70. Page 33 half-sheet ("The Sea Chase").

[J] "The Sea (Main Book Two) Section One." Typescript, pencil corrections, 82 pages. Pagination 1–4, 4, 5–21, 21a–e, 22–52, insert, 53–73. Sheet of word counts and letter to EH at end.

[K] "The Sea Main Book Three"

[i] Typescripts and originals, two carbons, uncorrected. Pagination 1–265. Also photocopy with corrections in ink in unknown hand.

[ii] Manuscript in pencil, corrections, one paragraph in typescript, six pages. Pagination 1–4, 3, 3. Drafts for opening.

[iii] Typescript, pencil corrections, four pages. Pagination 6–9.

[iv] Typescript and manuscript in pencil, extensive corrections, 16 pages. Pagination 1–4, 4, 5–15.

[v] Typescript, pencil corrections, 23 pages. Pagination 211–22, 227–38. Note of instructions by EH after 222.

[vi] Typescript, pencil corrections, 30 pages. Pagination 84–114.

[vii] Typescript, pencil corrections, 30 pages. Pagination 84–114. Insert clipped to page 84. Similar but not identical to entry above.

[viii] Manuscript in pencil, three pages. Pagination 446–48. Draft of "Chapter 16."

[ix] Manuscript in pencil, four pages. Pagination 466–69.

[x] Manuscript in pencil, corrections, 43 pages. Pagination 516–28, insert, 529–56, [557].

[xi] Typescript, one page of instructions for names of characters.

[xii] Manuscript in pencil, one page, unidentified.

[L] "The Sea Chase." Typescript of excerpts for White House reading, April 19, 1962, with Frederic March's emphasis marks, 16 pages. Pagination i, 1–15. Also unmarked carbon and negative photostat.

18 [*THE SUN ALSO RISES*]

[A] Manuscript in ink. Seven small notebooks in paper wrappers, numbered I–VII by EH. EH has written in ink "Fiesta A Novel" on each wrapper, and noted places and dates of writing in top right hand corners. His Paris address also appears with slight variations as follows: "Ernest M. Hemingway 113 Rue Notre Dame des Champs Paris VI Francia."

[i] "Fiesta A Novel Book I Valencia July 23—Aug. 3." 47 ruled leaves written on both sides, unpaged. Opening on first leaf: "page 38– Niño de la Palma (continued from loose sheets)." Begins with "Chap II."

[ii] "Fiesta A Novel Book II Valencia Aug. 3— Madrid Aug. 5–6 San Sebastian Aug. 8–9—Hendaye Aug. 10–11–12 Août 1925." 40 ruled leaves written on both sides, unpaged.

[iii] "Fiesta A Novel Book III Hendaye Aug. 12–13–14–15–16–17—Paris Aug. 19–20 Book 3 *100 pages.*" 50 ruled leaves written on both sides, unpaged. Bit of typed doggerel on inserted envelope, plot outline on back of notebook for chapters XIII–XVIII. Also word count and travel expenses.

[iv] "Fiesta A Novel 4th Book IV Paris Aug. 20–21–22–23–24–25–26–27–28–29. [September lined out] August 1925." 100 ruled leaves written on both sides, 3½ pages in pencil. Notes and map of the Great Lakes scribbled on back.

[v] "Fiesta A Novel Book No. V finished Sept 9 Paris." 48 ruled leaves, ink, written on both sides. Ink and pencil corrections, unpaged. Third and fifth leaves, verso, and fourth and sixth, recto, are blank, corresponding to pages 6–7, 10–11. ("The grave's a fine and secret [*sic*] place / But none I think do there embrace" written on cover.)

[vi] "Fiesta A Novel Book VI Sept 9 Paris." 48 ruled leaves written on both sides, corrections in ink and pencil, extensive cuts toward the end, unpaged. "To the Editor": a letter written lengthwise on the last two pages in an unknown hand. Written by a woman who has been presented the ears of a bull. Almost certainly Hadley Hemingway.

[vii] "Fiesta A Novel Book VII." 42 ruled leaves [of 48], the last six leaves torn out, written on both sides of first two leaves, and recto of third, corresponding to pages 1–5. End of text noted: "The End. Paris— Sept. 21—1925." Contains two leaves upside-down in ink which appear to be later draft of opening to *The Sun Also Rises*.

[B] *"Fiesta A Novel."* Typescript, 34 pages, the first blank. Pagination [i], 1–31. Opening "I saw him for the first time. . . ."

[C] Notebook written on one page only with a line on the following page. Fragment of Duff-Twysden's conversation.

[D] Typescript and manuscript, carbon and ink, 38 pages, first, second, and fourth blank. Pagination [i–ix], 1–31. Pages 1–31 in ink, interlinear corrections. Facing page one of chapter one: "The grave's a fine and secret [sic] place but none I think do there embrace . . . Marvell." Names for characters listed on fifth page. (Cf. *Fiesta,* Book I.)

[E] "It was half past three. . . ." Typescript, corrected in type. Two pages, corrected in type. In the Hotel Montoya.

[F] "It was half past three in the afternoon. . . ." Typescript, original, corrections in ink, five pages. Pagination 1–5.

[G] "I saw him for the first time. . . ." "Chapter One" One page, ink correction. Description of Niño de la Palma.

[H] Typescript, original, in binder. Sparse corrections in ink. Pagination [i–iii], 2–118. First and last pages blank. Pencil epigraph inserted on title page: "You are all a lost generation—Gertrude Stein in conversation."

[I] Typescript, carbon, of above, uncorrected, without penciled epigraph.

[J] Typescript, carbon, uncorrected, loose in binder. Beginning with "Chapter eleven." Pagination [1]–222, Chapters 21 and 22 clipped together. In envelope labeled in hand of MH: "Early version 'The Sun Also Rises.'"

[K] Typescript, first ten pages original, rest mostly carbon, beginning with Chapter 11. Sparse ink and pencil corrections, 184 pages. Pagination 1–184. In original folder from typist noting costs, number of lines, and each typist's share of work. A very late draft.

[L] "This is a novel about a lady." Typescript, ink corrections, one page. Discarded beginning.

[M] Three galleys: discarded first two chapters of the novel, uncorrected. (Cf. Fitzgerald letter under MISCELLANEOUS ITEMS at end.)

19 *THREE STORIES AND TEN POEMS*

Typescript, carbon. Sparse corrections in pencil, not all by EH. Pagination i–iv, 1–7, [unpaged] 1–8, [unpaged] 1–18, [unpaged] 1–3, 5, 9, 4, 6, 7, 10, 8. [Pages left as found.] Apparently setting copy. (Letter enclosed from "International Secretarial Office, 47, Avenue de L'Opera, Paris," dated November 17, 1925. "Copy of Document with one carbon 1272 lines at Frs. 12-per 100 lines . . . . Frs. 152.")

20 [*TO HAVE AND HAVE NOT*]

[A] Typescript and manuscript in pencil. Various pagings. Pages 1–73 in typescript, uncorrected. Followed by same part of story, pages made up of tear sheets from *Cosmopolitan,* retitled: "Part One Chapter One —Harry Morgan Spring" in pencil. Word counts at bottom of column and some corrections. Pagination adapted from magazine: page 122 followed by 122–23 in manuscript. Part Two follows: "Harry Morgan and the fall," originally entitled "Prologue—Man and Alphabet Man." Typescript, pagination 1–13, followed by pages 14–15, manuscript in pencil. Corner of page 13 missing, affecting four lines of text.

[B] Typescript, original. Sparse corrections in pencil. 193 pages. Pagination 1–185, 185a,b,c, 186–89 on one sheet, 190–94. Pages 190–94 in pencil. Setting copy.

[C] Chapter 12, six page insert pagination 1–6, pagination begins again 24–7, 27, 28–65, unpaginated insert, 66–91, unpaginated insert, 92–105, 106 insert, 106–27, followed by two blank pages.

[D] Chapter 19, "Winter Haven for Writers—Part Four." Pagination 128–56 bis, 156, 157–60, 160, 161, 162, 162 bis, 162 ter ("a third time"), 163, 164–80, unpaginated insert, 194–203, unpaginated two page insert on Hart Crane and F. Scott Fitzgerald, unpublished, 204–58.

[E] Manuscript in pencil, beginning with Chapter 23. Pagination 1, unpaginated insert, 2–16A, 16B, 17–9, 278–341, 342–55, insert 356, unpaginated insert, 357, insert A page 258 [*sic*], 358–63, 364A, 364B, 365–78, unpaginated insert, 379–87, insert 388, 388–417, 416–30, 432–51. Page 431 skipped in numbering.

[F] Assorted fragments and drafts:

[i] "Chapter Forty—Thomas Bradley." Manuscript in pencil, corrections, four pages. Pagination 495–99.

[ii] "Chapter Forty—Thomas Bradley Makes His First Trip." Typescript. Pagination 168, 172–74.

[iii] Manuscript in pencil, 49 pages. Pagination 1–49.

[iv] Typescript, corrected in pencil. Pagination 54–60, 65–96, 152–67.

[v] Insert page 32—Chapter 15, manuscript in pencil. Pagination 1–7. Other manuscript pages in pencil: 33, 39, 53, 61, 64, 98, 99, 107, 108, 130, insert 150, insert 154.

[vi] Galley proofs with sparse pencil corrections. KW

[vii] Galley proofs, more heavily corrected. KW

[viii] Manuscript in pencil, three pages. Pagination 172–73, 173. Draft for ending.

21 *THE TORRENTS OF SPRING: A ROMANTIC NOVEL IN HONOR OF THE PASSING OF A GREAT RACE*

Typescript, original, ink corrections interlinear and marginal, 82 pages. Pagination [i–iv], 1–75. Inserts pasted on pages 45 and 47. Preface with note: "I will probably cut this out." Author's final note to the reader begins: "It took me ten days to write it. Has it been worth it?" On inner fold are notes for parts and chapters of the book, and on the back is holograph note: "Pauquina [?] in MS Wright—Sept 1923." Note clipped to folder: "New Chapter on new page 3 copies Friday morning."

22 *WINNER TAKE NOTHING*

[A] Typescript, mixed originals and carbons, numerous pencil and ink corrections, various pagings. Includes tear sheets from *Scribner's Magazine, This Quarter,* etc., for "Homage to Switzerland Part I," "A Clean Well-Lighted Place" (uncorrected), "The Sea Change" (four corrections), "The Gambler, the Nun and the Radio" (title changed, 3 corrections), "God Rest You Merry Gentlemen" (galley sheets for House of Books publication, substantial additions and corrections in ink), "A Natural History of the Dead" (page proofs from *Death in the Afternoon,* many deletions and corrections; also present in typescript with interlinear and marginal corrections in ink), "Wine of Wyoming" (one correction; also present in typescript with sparse ink and pencil corrections).

[B] Labeled in unknown hand "Complete Printer's copy for stories consisting of typescripts and printed pages from prior book or magazine publications, with numerous changes and additions by Hemingway."

[C] Galley proofs, 51 galleys, pencil corrections, and EH's instructions for different order to the stories. "The Light of the World," "A Natural History of the Dead," "The Gambler, the Nun, and the Radio," and "Fathers and Sons" substantially revised with significant additions to the texts. Various obscenities deleted by EH. KW

SHORT FICTION

23 "After the Storm"

[A] Manuscript in pencil, ink and pencil corrections, 25 pages. Pagination 1–25. Early draft, very different from published version. EH note on plot, verso of page 19.

[B] Manuscript in pencil, ink corrections, 14 pages. Pagination 14, 14–27. Fragment. Opens "I drifted over her with the boat . . ." Differs from final version.

24 "An Alpine Idyll"

[A] Manuscript in pencil, sparse corrections, 13 pages. Pagination 1–13.

[B] Typescript, original, pencil corrections, nine pages. Pagination 1–8, [9]. Note from typist included.

[C] Typescript, original, nine pages. Pagination 1–9. Uncorrected. In brown paper binder.

25 "The Autobiography of Alice B. Hemingway or Who Taught the Fifth Grade Then? Or Finally She Bit on the Nail Again, a Little" (*unpublished*)

Typescript, corrections, six pages. Pagination 1–6. Burlesque in first person.

26 "Before the Season" [*sic*]

Typescript, carbon, extensive pencil corrections, seven pages. Pagination 1–7. Published as "Out of Season."

27 "Big Two Hearted River"

[A] Manuscript in ink, corrections, 102 pages. Pagination 1–99. Three-page insert between pages 3–4. "Chapter Two" corrected to "Part Two" page 58. Early draft.

[B] Manuscript in pencil, corrections, ten pages. Pagination [1–2], 3–10. A very early draft for the end of the story.

[C] Proofs, corrected by Hadley Hemingway. From *This Quarter*, May, 1925.

28 "A Broken Heart"

Typescript, interlinear corrections in ink and pencil, eight pages. Pagination 1–8. Long revision in ink on last page. Considerably revised this became "Ten Indians."

29 "The Bullfighters. A Story"

Typescript and pencil, interlinear corrections in ink and pencil, 42 pages. Pagination [i], 1–41. This became "The Undefeated."

30 "A Canary for One: A Story"

[A] Typescript and pencil, 11 pages. Pagination 1–7, 11–14. Verso of page 12 has penciled insert. One draft and part of another. Very early version told in first person.

[B] Typescript, original, corrections, seven pages. Pagination 1–7. Torn in many fragments, re-assembled with scotch tape. Large piece of first page missing.

31 "Cat in the Rain"

[A] Manuscript in ink, ten pages. Pagination 1–10. Top right hand corner of first sheet: "First Draft original manuscript March, 1924 E.M.H."

[B] Manuscript in ink, corrections, 19 pages. Pagination 1–19. Another title, "The Poor Kitty," crossed out. Close to published version.

[C] Manuscript in ink, three pages. Pagination [1], 1–2. Opens "There were only two Americans. . . ."

32   "Crime and Punishment"   (*unpublished*)

Manuscript in pencil, corrections, 11 pages. Pagination 1–11. One line on verso of page five. Story about homosexual sailor, set in 1932.

33   "Cross Country Snow"

[A] Typescript, original, ink corrections, eight pages. Pagination 1–8.

[B] Typescript, carbon, and pencil, pencil and ink corrections, 11 pages. Pagination 1–11.

[C] Manuscript in pencil, one page. Pagination 12. Possibly last page of draft above.

34 ["The Cross Roads"]   (*unpublished*)

Manuscript in ink and pencil, corrections. Pagination 1–18, 18 bis, 19–30, 32, 32–36. Page 31 misnumbered 32. Pages 1–24 in ink, 25–36 in pencil. Photocopy of above also present. World War II narrative. Renamed "Black-Ass at the Crossroads."

35 "The day we drove back from Nancy to Paris after being interrogated by the inspector general"
           (*unpublished*)

Manuscript, 16 pages. Fictionalized account of EH's interrogation about noncivilian behavior as war correspondent. Photocopy also present.

36 ["The Doctor and the Doctor's Wife"]

[A] Manuscript in ink with corrections, 11 pages. Pagination 1–11. "Original manuscript. First Draft. April 7, 1924, Paris EMH." Note by EH on verso last page: "Don't feel disgraced if you're a cuckold. Even a bull has horns."

[B] Manuscript in ink, corrections, 18 pages, the last blank. Pagination 1–17.

37 "The End of Something"

Manuscript in ink, 20 pages, sparse corrections. Pagination 1–20. Paris address, 113 Rue Notre Dame des Champs.

38 "Fifty Grand (A Story)"

Typescript, ink and pencil corrections, four pages. Pagination 1–3, 37. Top right corner of first sheet torn off, apparently by EH, but present. On it, EH wrote: "1st 3 pages of story mutilated by Scott Fitzgerald with [?] his"—the rest illegible. First 2½ pages deleted from story as published. Original title, "Jack," crossed out. On margin, page three, "D [?] yourself" in Fitzgerald's hand.

39 "Flower of the Party"

[A] Manuscript in pencil, 48 pages, interlinear and marginal corrections. Pagination 1–6, 6, 7–12, 9–26, 26 bis, 27–41 originally numbered 31–37. Damp stained. Published as "Nobody Ever Dies!" in *Cosmopolitan,* March, 1939.

[B] Typescript, uncorrected; "5074 words" in ink, upper right corner; 20 pages. Pagination 1–20. Attached note by typist.

40 "The galleria in Milan . . ."   (*unpublished*)

Manuscript in pencil on folded sheets. Pagination I–XXII. Long poker game.

41 "Get a Seeing-eyed Dog"

[A] Typescript, original, pencil corrections, six pages. Pagination 1–6. Published in *Atlantic Monthly,* November, 1957.

[B] Typescript, 11 pages. Pagination 1–11, uncorrected carbon.

42 "God Rest You Merry Gentlemen"

[A] Manuscript in pencil, corrections interlinear and marginal, 11 pages. Pagination 1–11.

[B] Typescript, original, five pages, sparse pencil and ink corrections. Pagination 1–5. First appeared, 1933; appeared later in same year as story in *Winner Take Nothing.*

[C] Typescript carbon, corrections in ink, five pages. Pagination 1–5. Upper left in ink: "Ernest Hemingway Key-West Florida. 1st U.S. Serial Rights only (all names are fictitious)."

43 "The Great Man"

Typescript and ink, interlinear corrections; 19 pages,
the first three in typescript, remainder in ink. Pagination 1–4, 6–20, page 5 missing. Early draft of "The
Battler."

44 "Good News from the Mainland"   (*unpublished*)

[A] Manuscript in pencil, nine pages. Pagination 1–6,
insert 7, 7–8. Stephen and Mr. Wheeler in Key West.
Similar to "I Guess Everything Reminds You of Something" (item 51).

[B] Typescript, original, five pages, corrected in pencil.
Pagination 1–5.

45 "The Happy Ending"

Typescript, pencil corrections, 25 pages. Pagination
1–25. Draft of "The Snows of Kilimanjaro."

46 "He had been in swimming. . . ."   (*unpublished*)

Typescript uncorrected, two pages. Unpaginated.
Sketch of Nick's wedding.

47 "He was quite thin and blind. . . ."   (*unpublished*)

Manuscript in pencil, four pages. Pagination 1–4. Draft for story about "Doc Kling." Mentions Kansas City *Star* and ambulances.

48 "Hills Like White Elephants. A Story"

Manuscript in pencil, corrections, 12 pages. Pagination 1–12. Signed, with Paris address. Note at bottom of last page in hand of EH: "Mss. for Pauline—well, well, well."

49 "Homage to Switzerland"

[A] Manuscript in pencil, interlinear corrections, 38 pages. Pagination [i–ii], 2–7, [8–37].

[B] Typescript, heavy pencil corrections, 14 pages. Pagination 1–14. In ink, upper right hand corner: "Ernest Hemingway, L Bar T Ranch, Cooke City, Montana. First English language serial rights *only*. Please return mss. with proof."

50 "The Home Front"

"The Stooges of Stalin" lined out. Typescript, pencil corrections, six pages. Pagination 1–6. In envelope labeled: "E.H.—The Home Front Story."

51 "I Guess Everything Reminds You of Something. A Story"   (*unpublished*)

[A] Manuscript in pencil, stapled together, 15 pages. Pagination 1–15. Similar to "Good News from the Mainland."

[B] Typescript, original, corrections, eight pages. Pagination 1–8.

52 "Ignorance or a Puritan Courtship"   (*unpublished*)

Typescript, uncorrected, three pages, torn in half. Another draft, eight pages, the last blank. A burlesque of a manuscript in an unknown hand, opening "Amalgamated Steele was a handsome man."

53 "In Another Country"

[A] Typescript, carbon, pencil corrections, some marginal additions, seven pages. Pagination 1–7.

[B] Manuscript in pencil, one page. Opens "In the fall of the year . . ." Sentence drafts.

[C] "In Another Country—Two. A Story" Typescript, pencil corrections, ten pages. Pagination 1–10. Near-final draft of what became "Now I Lay Me."

[D] "In the fall the war was there. . . ." Typescript, pencil corrections, interlinear and marginal, four pages. Draft of opening.

54   ["Indian Camp"]

Manuscript in ink and pencil, corrected. 16 pages in ruled notebook, written on recto and verso. Unpaginated early draft. On cover: "Ernest Hemingway Chartres September 27, 1925."

55   "In those days everyone was fond of my father. . . ."

(Cf. "This is the story of Eldred Johnstone. . . ." item 88.)

56   "Indian Country and the White Army" *(unpublished)*

Manuscript in ink and pencil, 25 pages, interlinear pencil corrections. Pagination 1–25; pages 1–10 in ink, 13–25 in pencil. Rejected title: "The Limited Objective." World War II narrative opening "The Forest of the Ardennes was all Indian country." Photocopy present.

57   "It was getting hot. . . ."   *(unpublished)*

Nick fishing and thinking of bullfighting, art, literature, etc.; loosely related to "Big Two-Hearted River," item **27**.

58   "Italy, 1927"

Manuscript, three pages. Unpaginated draft. Appeared in *New Republic,* May 18, 1927. Later became part of "Che Ti Dice La Patria?" (See "A Meal in Spezia," item 65.)

59   "The Kansas City train stopped. . . ."   (*unpublished*)

Typescript, two pages. Pagination 1–2. Sketch of Nick's first sight of Mississippi River.

60   "The Killers"

Typescript and pencil, 18 pages, first nine in typescript, last nine in pencil. Pagination 1–9, 1–9. Bottom of page nine torn away. Rejected title, "The Matadors," lined out. Top right-hand corner: "Madrid—May 1926 Ernest Hemingway" On right hand margin: "For Uncle Gus! Written between 215 and 8 [?] pm." "Petoskey" is changed to "Summit," "Wop" to "Swede," "Nerone" to "Andreson."

61   "Landscape with Figures"   (*unpublished*)

"In the Old Homestead" lined out. Typescript and pencil, pencil corrections, 32 pages. Pagination 1–27, one page insert in pencil between page one and two, three pages insert in pencil between page five and six, one page insert in pencil between page six and seven. Inserts and pages 9–27 in pencil. War fiction set in Spain, "Edwin Henry" protagonist. Opens "It was very strange in that house."

62   "The Last Good Country"   (*unpublished*)

[A] (Title by MH.) In folder labeled: "Escape—upper Michigan unfinished" by MH.

[B] Note by Malcolm Cowley: "An unfinished story Upper Michigan Nick Adams and Sister Littless (Ursula) Escape from Game Wardens." First part of a Nick Adams novel.

[C] Manuscript in ink, pencil and typescript, corrections in ink and pencil, 110 loose pages. Pagination 1–3, 3–8, 8, 8, 9, 9–102, 102. Two page insert after page one. Page 53 dated July 23, '52. Page 88 dated April '55. Page 100 dated July 20, '58. Pages 1–3 in typescript removed from fragment noted below. Photocopy present.

[D] Fragment labeled: "First Version" (MH?). Typescript, original, pencil corrections interlinear and marginal, ten pages. Pagination 4–13.

[E] Draft for another start, manuscript in pencil. Two pages.

[F] "Different Start." Typescript, carbon, uncorrected, one page. New beginning to the story.

63 "The Light of the World"

[A] Manuscript in pencil, four pages. Pagination
23–26. Page 24 torn neatly in half, lower part inserted
before page 25. Draft for conclusion of the story.

[B] Typescript, late draft, sparse ink corrections, seven
pages. Pagination 1–7. "By Ernest Hemingway Cooke-
Montana . . ."

64 "A Man of the World"

Typescript, uncorrected, six pages. Pagination 1–6.
Published in *Atlantic Monthly,* November, 1957.

65 "A Meal in Spezia" [Also titled "Italy 1927"]

Typescript, pencil corrections, five pages. Pagination
1–5. Drawing of an arch [?] on verso of last page.
Second part of "Che Ti Dice La Patria?"

66 ["A Medieval Chronicle"]

"There were young knights. . . ." Manuscript in pencil,
one page. Epigraph composed by EH for Martha Gell-
horn, *A Stricken Field,* N.Y., 1940.

67   "Mr. and Mrs. Smith by Ernest Hemingway 113 Rue Notre Dame des Champs Paris VI, France."

Manuscript in ink, sparse interlinear corrections, 15 pages. Pagination 1–15. This became "Mr. and Mrs. Elliot."

68   "The Monument"   (*unpublished*)

Manuscript in pencil, ink corrections, 19 pages. Pagination 1–19. World War II narrative opening "It was that evening after the bloodless taking of . . ." Autobiographical. Photocopy present.

69   "My Old Man"

Typescript, carbon, pencil corrections, 14 pages. Pagination 1–14. Has been folded in envelope. One story of two that survived 1922 theft of manuscript from Hadley Hemingway. Also uncorrected carbon.

70   ["A Natural History of the Dead"]

Manuscript in pencil, one page written on both sides. Opens "The thing I remember most about a battlefield . . ."

71   "Nick was undressing in the tent"

Manuscript in ink, eight pages. Pagination 1–8. Nick on camping trip with Uncle George and his father. Rejected opening to "Indian Camp."

72   "Night Before Battle"

[A] Typescript, profuse interlinear and marginal corrections in pencil, 36 pages. Pagination 1–31, 31 bis, 32 [insert page 33], 33–4. Silverfish damage affecting signature and title. Penciled pages inserted between pages 1–2, 32–33. Appeared in *Esquire,* February, 1939.

[B] Typescript, carbon, pencil corrections, 43 pages. Pagination 1–43. Corner first page missing. EH: "First U.S. serial rights only. 10,947 words."

73   "Now I Lay Me"

Typescript, carbon, pencil corrections, marginal and interlinear, nine pages. Pagination 1–9. (See also "In Another Country—II," item 53C.)

74   "One Night Last Summer"

Typescript, carbon in purple ink, a few ink corrections, seven pages. Pagination 1–7. In ink, top left corner of first sheet, name and Paris address. A nearly final draft of what became "Indian Camp," item 54. Published April 1924 in *transatlantic review* as "Work in Progress."

75 ["One Trip Across"]

Manuscript in pencil, seven pages. Pagination 1–2, 4–7, 9. Draft of story which appeared in *Cosmopolitan,* April 1934. Later became Part I of *To Have and Have Not,* item 20.

76 "The Petoskey road ran straight up the hill from Grandpa Bacon's farm." *(unpublished)*

Manuscript and typescript, five pages. First page in typescript, the rest in ink. Nick Adams and the Indians? Also one manuscript page in ink, pagination 5, opening "The Green boy, Eddy . . ."

77 "A Pursuit Race"

Typescript, red, pencil corrections, six sheets. Pagination 1–6.

78   "The Revolutionist"

Typescript, five pages. Various starts.

79   "A Room on the Garden Side"   (*unpublished*)

Typescript, carbon, 11 pages. Pagination 1–11, pages 7–11 renumbered in ink. Opens "We were all up in the room at the Ritz." Conversation with Charles Ritz, wine drinking. Quotation from Baudelaire.

80   "The Sea Change"

[A] Manuscript in pencil, ink corrections, 13 pages. Pagination i–ii, 2–11.

[B] Manuscript in ink, pencil corrections, 13 pages. Pagination 1–13. Differs markedly from above.

[C] Manuscript in pencil, one page written on both sides. Draft beginning "It was the end of summer. . . ."

[D] Manuscript in ink. One paragraph from "The Sea Change," opening "What do the punks drink, James?"

81   "The Short Happy Life of Francis Macomber"

[A] Four manuscript fragments of drafts in pencil, opening "Of course by the third day . . ." Four pages. Pagination 1–4. Extremely early draft.

[B] "She looked like all those pictures. . . ." Five pages. Pagination 1–5.

[C] "There was a lantern in the dining tent. . . ." Three pages. Pagination 1–3.

[D] "The sky is very high there. . . ." Four pages. Pagination 1–4. See also entry 7, *The Fifth Column and the First Forty-Nine Stories,* for additional typescript.

82   "A Simple Enquiry"

Typescript, red, pencil corrections, four pages. Pagination 1–4. Also corrected carbon.

83   "Soldier's Home"

[A] Manuscript in ink and pencil, heavily corrected, 29 pages. Pagination 1–29. Pages 6 and 17 are half sheets. Very early draft.

[B] Typescript, carbon, 11 pages. Pagination 1–11. One pencil correction. Piece torn out of middle right hand margin throughout. With damaged envelope from Harper and Brothers postmarked October 13, 1924.

84   "The Story of the Faithful Bull"

[A] Typescript, original, uncorrected, four pages. Pagination 1–4. Published as "The Faithful Bull" in *Holiday*, March, 1951.

[B] Typescript, carbon, interlinear corrections in ink, four pages. Pagination 1–4.

85   "Summer People"   (*unpublished*)

Manuscript in ink, corrections, 40 pages. Pagination 1–40. Nick Adams story, probably the first written. Listed by EH in 1926 notebook as "Uncompleted."

86   "Ten Indians"

[A] Typescript, pencil corrections, eight pages. Pagination 1–8. "Madrid" in pencil on top right corner.

[B] Manuscript in ink, corrections, 14 pages in notebook. Draft with different ending. Cf. "A Broken Heart," item 28.

87   "They got off the train at Seney. There was no station."

Manuscript in ink, three pages. Pagination 1–3. Description of burned-out town. Draft for early version of "Big Two-Hearted River," item 27.

88 "This is the story of the death of Eldred John-
    stone. . . ."   (*unpublished*)

    Notebook containing 16 pages in pencil. An uncom-
    pleted story set in mountains on Austro-Italian front.

89 "In those days everyone was fond of my Father. . . ."
                                                (*unpublished*)

    On verso pages of notebook described in item 88, in
    pencil, another incomplete story concerning the suicide
    of a child's father. Child's name was "Nick," crossed
    out and replaced by "Edward Thompson." Early draft
    of "Fathers and Sons," item 91?

90 "Today is Friday"

    Typescript, pencil and ink corrections, five pages. Pag-
    ination 1–5. Lined-out titles: "One More for the Naz-
    arene," "The Seed of the Church." This short play first
    published as a pamphlet, 1926; then included in *Men
    Without Women,* 1927.

91 "The Tomb of My Grandfather"

    Manuscript in pencil, corrections, 25 pages. Pagination
    1–7A, 7B, 8–24. Published as "Fathers and Sons."

92   "The train moved through the hot valley. . . ."

(unpublished)

Manuscript in ink, sparse corrections, eight pages, first two blank. Pagination [i–ii], 1–6.

93   ["The Undefeated"]

[A] Manuscript in pencil in four unruled notebooks written on recto only.

> [i] First notebook, 16 leaves. Pagination recto-verso 1–32. Pages 27–32 blank. Opens "Zurito leaned forward on the barrera. . . ."
>
> [ii] "2nd booklet," 16 leaves unpaginated, last two blank.
>
> [iii] "3rd booklet," 16 leaves unpaginated, last seven blank.
>
> [iv] "4th booklet," 15 leaves unpaginated, last leaves torn out. Text ends: "he heard somebody very heavily. . . ."

[B] Manuscript in pencil, corrections, 16 pages. Pagination 1–3, 3 bis, 14–15, 16/17, 28–35, 41. Three copies of page 41 present in typescript. At the head of first sheet note by EH: "After fourth booklet."

[C] Typescript, ink corrections, 41 pages. Pagination 1–41. Note by EH: "First typewritten manuscript Ernest Hemingway for G. A. Pfeiffer." Cf. "The Bullfighters," item 29.

94 ["Up in Michigan"]

[A] Manuscript in pencil, interlinear corrections, seven pages. Pagination 1–7, tear in upper right corner of first sheet affecting a word of text. Begins "A steep sandy road ran down the hill. . . ." This story also survived the 1922 theft of manuscript from Hadley.

[B] Typescript, ink and pencil corrections, eight pages. Pagination 1–8. Apparently earlier than penciled draft above. Upper left corner first page: "Ernest Hemingway 74 Rue du Cardinal Lemoine Paris."

[C] Typescript, pencil corrections, six pages. Pagination 1–6.

95 "A Way You'll Never Be"

[A] Typescript, pencil corrections, marginal and interlinear, 15 pages. Paginated 1–15. Vertical tear through all pages.

[B] Manuscript in pencil, two pages. Draft for fragment of the story. Opens "As I came into the town . . ."

96 ["Wine of Wyoming"]

[A] Typescript and pencil, pencil and ink corrections, 24 pages. Pagination 1–24; 1–12 typescript, 13–24 in pencil.

[B] Typescript carbon, corrected sparsely in ink, 18 pages. Pagination 1–18.

[C] Typescript, 18 pages. Pagination 1–18. Corrected sparsely in ink. First page ink stained, browned, crumpled.

97 "The woman came out to the road from the big farm house when we stopped the jeep."   (*unpublished*)

Typescript, original, pencil corrections, three pages. Pagination 1–3. Another draft, typescript, three pages. Unpaginated. About tanks. Part of "The Cross Roads," item 34?

JOURNALISM
and other Non-fiction

98 "And so they talked. Then they talked some more."

Typescript, carbon, six half-sheets. Pagination 1–6. Set in Toronto. Mentions various newspaper men. For the most part published in Carlos Baker's *Ernest Hemingway: a Life Story.*

99 ["And to the United States"]

Manuscript in ink, 12 pages. Pagination 1–12. Published in *transatlantic review,* May–June, 1924.

100 "The Art of the Short Story"   *(unpublished)*

Manuscript in ink, four pages. Unpaged. Followed by manuscript in pencil, 47 pages. Paginated 1–47. One additional page, word counts ("5868" total), dated "13/6/59." Introduction to projected collection of short stories, unpublished.

101 "The author, whose portrait, drawn by a man . . ."

Typescript, one page, torn in two pieces. Sketch for George Schreiber's *Portraits and Self-Portraits,* Boston, 1936.

102 "Bull-fighting Business"

Typescript, occasional corrections in pencil, 31 pages. Pagination 1–21, 1–10. Last ten pages consist of 12 penciled footnotes. Published in *Fortune,* March, 1930, as "Bullfighting, Sport and Industry."

103 "Conrad, Optimist and Moralist"

Seven pages. Pagination 2–8. Corrections, interlinear. Published in *transatlantic review,* October, 1924, as "Conrad."

104 "Cuban Fishing"

[A] Typescript, original, pencil corrections interlinear and marginal, seven pages. Unpaginated. Published in Brian Vesey-Fitzgerald and Francesca Lamonte, Eds., *Game Fish of the World,* London, Brussels: 1949.

[B] Typescript, carbon, sparse pencil corrections, new pages. Pagination 1–9. With two letters from Francesca Lamonte of the American Museum of Natural History.

105 "Eulogy to the American Dead in Spain"

Typescript, carbon, uncorrected, two pages. Pagination iii–iv. Dated: "February 14, 1939." Published in *New Masses,* February 14, 1939.

106 "Every now and then I read some highbrow article by someone or other. . . ."   (*unpublished*)

Nine pages, ink corrections. Pagination 1–9. Attack on critics.

107 ["The Great Blue River"]

[A] Early draft in pencil and original typescript, interlinear corrections, 20 pages. Pagination 1–12, 13 bis, 13–19. Published in *Holiday,* July, 1949.

[B] Typescript, carbon, a few corrections in pencil, 14 pages. Pagination 1–14. With this a note in pencil beginning "Deal was called off at my request. . . ."

108 ["H. M.'s Loyal State Department"]

Typed carbon of cable, four pages. Pagination 1–4. To "esquisyn Chicago." With second cable: "Check carefully for libel." KW. Published in *Ken,* June 6, 1938.

109   "How I Broke With John Wilkes Booth"

[A] Typescript, eight pages, last one blank, few pencil corrections. Pagination [1], 2, [1], 2–5, [6]. Published in *The New Yorker* as "My Own Life," February 12, 1927.

[B] Typescript, four pages, few typed and penciled corrections. Pagination 1–4.

[C] Typescript, original, uncorrected, with check stub for $75.00 from *The New Yorker*.

110   "In this town there are people who have never been in any other part of town."   (*unpublished*)

Manuscript in pencil, four pages. Pagination 1–4. Essay on Key West, Florida. KW

111   Introduction to James Charters, *This Must Be the Place,* London, 1934

Manuscript in pencil, nine pages. Unpaginated. On last sheet: "Ernest Hemingway. Serengetti Plains, December Tanganyika. 1933"

112   "It has been a long time since the children have been in these columns. . . ."   *(unpublished)*

A conversation with his boys at time of the Spanish War. About his being "tool of Stalin."

113   ["Marlin off Cuba"]

Typescript, carbon, pencil corrections, 35 pages, last page in pencil. Pagination 1–35. Published as "Marlin off the Morro: a Cuban Letter," *Esquire,* Autumn, 1933.

114   "Monologue to the Maestro"

Manuscript in pencil, two pages. Pagination 5–6. Published in *Esquire,* October, 1935.

115   "My Life in the Bull Ring with Donald Ogden Stewart"   *(unpublished)*

[A] Typescript, ink corrections, five pages. Response to *Chicago Tribune's* 1924 claim that EH and Stewart had been gored in Spain. The clipping attached.

[B] Typescript, sparse ink and pencil corrections, six pages. With letter to *Vanity Fair,* undated.

116 "Notes on Dangerous Game by Ernest Hemingway 1st serial rights only. Third Tanganyika Letter Mbula Hills. Tanganyika. Above Lake Manyara."

Manuscript in ink, corrections interlinear and marginal, 14 pages. Pagination 1–14. Written on verso of letter sheets from "Svenska Amerika Linen M.S. *Gripsholm*." Published in *Esquire,* July, 1934.

117 "The Real Spaniard"

Typescript, original, sparse corrections. Published in *Boulevardier* I, viii (October, 1927), 6.

118 ["Sailfish off Mombasa: A Key West Letter"]

Manuscript in ink and pencil, 18 pages. Pagination 1–14, four page insert in pencil between pages one and two, page 11 torn in half. Note at beginning: "By Ernest Hemingway. . . . You Read it in February, labeled March, written in January." Published in *Esquire,* March, 1935.

19   "Second Tanganyika Letter Mbuli Mbuli Hills Tangan-
     yika by Ernest Hemingway 1st serial rights only."

     Manuscript in ink, sparse corrections, 17 pages. Pagi-
     nation 1–17. On pink, deckled wove paper. (Manuscript
     Label clipped on: "Lion Hunting" in unknown hand.)
     Published in *Esquire,* June, 1934.

20   "Senoras y Senores (Dar la gracias, etc.)"

     Manuscript in pencil, three pages, signed. Pagination
     1–3. Speech entirely in Spanish on presentation of
     Nobel Prize Medal to the shrine of the Virgen del
     Cobre in 1956.

21   ["The Shot"]

     [A] Typescript, carbon, pencil corrections, seven pages.
     Pagination 1–3, 2–6. Published in *True,* April, 1951.

     [B] Typescript, carbon. Slight corrections in pencil,
     eight pages. Pagination 1–8.

     [C] Typescript, one page. Opening page.

122   Toronto *Star*

Notes and typescript and background material for Toronto *Star* pieces including:

[i] "Franco-German." Typescript, carbon, of parts 4–9, 32 pages. Various pagings. Sparse corrections in type and pencil.

[ii] "Clemenceau." Typescript, damaged, corrected in type, 10 pages. Pagination [1–2], 2, 4–10, [11]. Typed nonsense about "fingernail harbour," Maine, laid in after page 10.

[iii] Folders of notes for articles on Sudbury Coal Company; Lausanne, Switzerland; Les Avants, Switzerland (two articles); Constantinople; American Relief Work; Quick Assets and Dead; Condensing the Classics; Prohibition; Kingston, Ontario; and two folders of various drafts and related material concerning Lloyd George, with a large quantity of manuscript notes taken during an interview with the subject on golf course. Also an untitled article for INS by-lined "John Hadley" on the Crown Prince of Rumania. Pencil corrections interlinear and marginal throughout.

123   "So my brain being in this damaged condition. . ."

Manuscript in ink, three pages. Pagination 1–3. Passage on Cohn and Schine for "The Christmas Gift," *Look*, April 20, May 4, 1954.

124 ["There She Breaches! or Moby Dick off the Morro"]

Typescript, 13 pages. Pagination 1–11. Pages 10–11 in pencil. Three page insert between seven and eight in pencil. Corrections interlinear and marginal. Published in *Esquire,* May, 1936.

125 "They say that you can never go back. . . ."
(unpublished)

Typescript, original, pencil corrections, three pages. Pagination 1–3. (On being accident prone; refers to Madrid siege.)

126 "When I was a boy I answered advertisements. . . ."
(unpublished)

Typescript, carbon, five pages. Unpaginated. KW

127 "Who Murdered the Vets?"

Typescript, original, with pencil corrections and additions, seven pages. Unpaginated. On veterans drowned in hurricane at Matecumbe Key, 1935. Published in *New Masses,* XVI, September 17, 1935. KW

128   "You can be right reader. Papa doesn't care about being right anymore."   *(unpublished?)*

Manuscript in ink, three pages. Pagination 1, [blank page], 2. Interlinear corrections. Unidentified journalism. (Mostly on Paris, also Joyce.)

POETRY

129   "Advice to my son"

[A] Manuscript in ink. Published as "Advice to a Son" in *Omnibus: Almanach auf das Jahr 1932,* Berlin, and Düsseldorf, 1932.

[B] Typescript, "Advice to a Son."

130   "All armies are the same. . . ."   (*unpublished*)

Manuscript in pencil, corrected. (Perhaps an addition to "Battle," item 133.)

131   "Along With Youth"

Typescript, two carbons, corrected. Different drafts.

132   "At Night I Lay with You"   (*unpublished*)

Manuscript in pencil, two lines only.

133 ["Battle"]

Typescript, uncorrected. Published as "Champs d'Honneur."

134 "Bird of Night"   (*unpublished*)

[A] Typescript. Two drafts, one untitled, opening "Cover my eyes with your pinions." Corrected.

[B] Typescript, corrected. Chicago address.

135 "Black-Ass Poem After Talking to Pamela Churchill"
                                       (*unpublished*)

Opening "We leave them all quite early when dislike overcomes our love. . . ." Dated "20/12/49 Ritz Hotel EH."

136 "Blood is thicker than water"

Five lines in pencil, published in Carlos Baker's *Ernest Hemingway: a Life Story,* p. 66.

137 "Captives"

[A] Typescript. Signed in pencil "Ernest M. Hemingway."

[B] Typescript, carbon.

138 "Champs d'Honneur"

Typescript, carbon. Same as "Battle," item 133.

139   "The City stinks and crawls with life. . . ."

                                                         (*unpublished*)

Typescript. Two copies. Similar to "Flat Roofs," item 143.

140   "Country Poem With Little Country"   (*unpublished*)

Dated "20/12/49 Ritz Hotel—EH" Opens "When gin is gone and all is over . . ."

141   "Defense of Luxembourg"   (*unpublished*)

Manuscript in pencil, two pages. Pagination 1–2. Also five typescripts. World War II poem. Opens "So now, alive . . ."

142   "First Poem to Mary in London"

[A] Typescript, original, typed on both sides. Paper much worn from folding and handling. Alternate title, "Who Serves My Lord Truth," crossed out. Published in *Atlantic,* August, 1965.

[B] Typescripts, two carbons, uncorrected, three sheets each. Pagination 1–3.

[C] Four typescripts, one photostat negative.

[D] Carbon of introduction, and galley proof, for appearance in *Atlantic*. Also photocopy of typescript.

143   "Flat Roofs"   (*unpublished*)

Typescript, carbon, uncorrected.

144   "For the harlot has a hard lot"   (*unpublished*)

Typescript, uncorrected.

145   *Four Poems by Ernest Hemingway*

Galley proofs. "On August 31, 1930 there were printed privately for the prevention of piracy 12 copies of *Four Poems,* for E.H. by L.H.C. [Louis Henry Cohn] This is Number   ."

146   "Grass smooth on the prairie . . ."   (*unpublished*)

Typescript.

147   "Heroes," "Battle," and "D'Annunzio"

Typescript. First and last titles *unpublished.*

148   "I think that I have never trod on anything as swell as sod. . . ."   (*unpublished*)

Manuscript in ink.

149   "In a magazine I saw a picture of a trench club. . . ."
       (*unpublished*)

Typescript, three pages. Pagination 1–3.

150 "In the rain in the rain in the rain"

Typescript, two pages, carbon. Draft for "The Soul of Spain," item 180.

151 "It is cool at night on the roofs of the city. . . ."
(*unpublished*)

Typescript, one page. Addressed 100 E. Chicago Avenue. Same as "Flat Roofs."

152 "Killed. Piave—June 15, 1918"   (*unpublished*)

Typescripts, two drafts, pencil corrections in first. Date changed to July 8, 1918, in second draft, addressed 100 E. Chicago Avenue.

153 "Kipling," "L'Envoi," "Stevenson," "Robert Graves"
(*unpublished*)

Typescript, uncorrected.

154 "The Lady Poets with Footnotes"

Typescript, pencil corrections.

155 "Lines to a girl 5 days after her 21st birthday"
(*unpublished*)

Manuscript in violet pencil, seven ruled sheets, stapled together. Opening "Back to the palace and home to a store she travels the fastest who travels alone."

156   Four poems on torn off cover of Patrick Hamilton's novel *Hangover Square*. [Entries 157–160 refer to the four poems.]

Note on front end paper by EH: "Verses written after the Battle of Hürtgen Forest, with a few lines dealing with Wirth and Giessenich. Possibly something about Grosshau."

157   "Lines to a Great Beauty"

Opening "Thy beauty shall always be found. . . ."

158   "Lines to his very beautiful wife"

Opening "The worms that ate our other friends . . ."

159   "Lines to M. and her surgeon"

Opening "Your slit . . ."

160   "Grosshau"

Opening "When Lightning Joe imperiously called . . ."

161   "Lines to a young lady on her having very nearly won a Vogel"   (*unpublished*)

[A] Manuscript in pencil, one page on both sides, and two typescripts. All vary. Typescripts uncorrected. In manuscript, "Fogel."

[B] Manuscript in pencil and typescript, one page.

162   "Little Mr. Wilson . . ."   (*unpublished*)

Manuscript in pencil. Poem on Edmund Wilson's novel *I Thought of Daisy.*

163   "Lord Curzon does not love. . . ."

Manuscript in pencil, one page, written on both sides. Part of item 182, "They all made Peace. What is Peace?"

164   "Montparnasse"

[A] Typescripts, two copies, many ink corrections and additions.

[B] Typescript, ink corrections, also uncorrected carbon.

165   ["Neothomist Poem"]

[A] Typescript, corrected. Much longer than published version.

[B] Three pages of drafts in notebook dated 1925/26. Also list of stories completed, uncompleted, sold and unsold, and notes on correspondence and forwarded manuscripts.

[C] Manuscript in pencil, one page, heavily corrected. In notebook containing four pages of penciled notes and a poem opening "And everything the author knows . . ." Similar to "Valentine."

166 "Night comes down with soft and drowsy plumes. . . ." (*unpublished*)

167 "Oklahoma"

Typescript, pencil corrections.

168 "The Poem is by Maera" (*unpublished*)

Manuscript in ink, three pages. Pagination 1–3.

169 "Poem to Mary (Second Poem)"

[A] In letter to "Dearest Pickle," "3:30 a.m." Manuscript in pencil, some corrections, eight pages, stapled together. Pagination 1–8. Early draft of second part. Published in *Atlantic,* August, 1965.

[B] Typescript, carbon, on pink paper, seven pages. Pagination 1–7.

[C] Typescript, carbon, corrections and additions. Pagination 8–9. Page 8 torn at bottom affecting two lines of text.

[D] Assorted manuscript drafts in pencil and typescript, 21 pages. Pagination 1–5, 5 bis, 5 ter, insert 1–3, three unnumbered pages of insert, 6–8, 8–9, 7–10.

[E] Seven typescripts and one negative photostat.

170 "Poem to Miss Mary"   (*unpublished*)

Typescript, original and carbon, pencil corrections, two copies. Opening "Now Mary you can face it good and face it in your widow-hood. . . ." Dated "Ritz Hotel —26/11/49—Room 86." Not the same as "Second Poem," item 169.

171 "Portrait of a Lady"   (*unpublished*)

Typescript.

172 "Riparto d'Assalto"

Typescript, two copies, original and carbon. Addressed "74 Rue du Cardinal Lemoine."

173 "The Road to Avallon"   (*unpublished*)

Manuscript in pencil, corrected. Signed and dated "22/12/49. EH Ritz Hotel Paris." Opens "The negro rich are nigger rich. . . ."

174 "Roosevelt"

Typescript, original and carbon.

175 "Schwartzwald"

In pencil, corrected. Opens "As white hairs in a silver foxes skin . . ."

176 "Shock Troops"   (*unpublished*)

Manuscript in pencil, uncorrected.

177 "Society Column"   (*unpublished*)

Opens "God is away for the summer." Typescript, addressed 100 East Chicago Avenue.

178 "Soldiers Never Do Die Well"

Manuscript in pencil. Draft for "Champs D'Honneur," item 138.

179 "Some day when you are picked up still . . ."
                                       (*unpublished*)

Manuscript in pencil, three pages.

180 "The Soul of Spain with McAlmon and Bird the Publishers. With Later Parts."

Typescript, five sheets, uncorrected.

181 "Storm Troops"   (*unpublished*)

[A] Manuscript in ink.
[B] Manuscript in pencil.

182   "They All Made Peace. What is Peace?"

Typescript, original, corrected, two pages.

183   "They Say It's Over"   (*unpublished*)

[A] Manuscript in pencil, corrections. Dated 1928.

[B] Manuscript in ink, pencil corrections, three pages. Pagination 1–3.

184   "They were such splendid negroes. . . ."
                                (*unpublished*)

Typescript, penciled notes on verso. Another draft present, opening "Hurray for Fonnie Richardson . . ." (Hadley Hemingway's sister), two pages. Pagination 1–2.

185   "To a Tragic Poetess"   (*unpublished*)

[A] Typescript, original, corrected, two pages. Pagination 1–2.

[B] Typescript, original, corrected in pencil, three pages. Pagination 1–3. With a corrected carbon.

[C] Typescript, carbon, penciled corrections, three pages. Pagination 1–3. Differs from two drafts above.

186   "To Chink whose trade is soldiering"   (*unpublished*)

Manuscript in pencil, corrections. (Chink is Eric Edward Dorman-Smith.)

187 "To Crazy Christian"   (*unpublished*)

Manuscript in pencil, on tablet board. Opening "There was a cat named Crazy Christian. . . ."

188 "To Good Guys Dead"   (*unpublished*)

Typescript, original. Opens "They sucked us in. . . ."

189 "To Will Davies"   (*unpublished*)

Typescript, original opening "There were two men to be hanged. . . ."

190 "Translations from the Esquimaux"   (*unpublished*)

Typescript, two four-line pieces, one called "Sea Otter."

191 "Travel Poem"   (*unpublished*)

Manuscript in pencil, badly stained: "22/12/49 Ritz Hotel Paris EH." Opening "Go Mary I would say to thee. . . ."

192 ["Ultimately" and other poems]

Notebook folder containing typescripts of: "Ultimately," "They all made Peace—What is Peace?" "Montparnasse," "Mitraigliatrice," "Oklahoma," "Oily Weather," "Roosevelt," "Captives," "Champs d'Honneur," "Riparto d'Assalto," "Along with Youth," "Chapter Heading," "The Age Demanded," "The Earnest Liberal's Lament," "The Soul of Spain" (photostat of Part II), "The Lady Poets with Footnotes" (photostat), "Neothomist Poem."

193 "Valentine to Mr. Dodd and Any of His Friends Who Are Oppressed."

[A] Two typescripts, corrected. Title varies slightly.

[B] Manuscript in pencil, corrections.

194 "The Young Liberal's Lament"

Typescript. Dedicated to Noel Buxton, Bertrand Russel [*sic*], and Oswald Garrison Villard. Other versions as follows:

[i] "The Earnest Liberal's Lament." Typescript.

[ii] "The Liberal's Prayer for Guidance." Typescript.

[iii] "The Liberal's Prayer for Guidance. (God is Love)." Typescript, uncorrected.

[iv] "To Earnest Liberals." Typescript, uncorrected, on sheet with "The Age Demanded."

FRAGMENTS

195 "After he was discharged from the marine corps . . ."

Manuscript in pencil, three pages. Last page doodles. "Soldier's Home"?

196 "After the Indians had lived in a house . . ."

Manuscript in pencil, four pages. Drafts of a single sentence for a Nick Adams story? Possibly "The Petoskey road . . ."

197 "All are damned twice, some more."

Manuscript in pencil, one page.

198 "All of the distances are changed in Kansas City now. . . ."

Manuscript in pencil, one page.

199 "The ambulances were Appersons. . . ."

Manuscript in pencil, two pages. Doc Fisher and Bill Wiggins.

200 "And now it is all over about a very great writer who had stopped writing because she was too lazy. . . ."

Typescript, pencil corrections, four pages. Satiric piece on Gertrude Stein. Complete?

201 "And when in the night when they shall wake why let them think of it themselves. . . ."

Manuscript in pencil, one page. Pagination 10.

202 "At night it was hotter than . . ."

Manuscript in pencil, one page.

203 "At Pamplona it had started to rain. . . ."

Five pages, pencil. In a car, wife's hypochondria.

204 "Benchley—A Comedy of Manners"

Manuscript in pencil, one page. Opens "Page One Act One Scene One." Characters are "Ernie" and "Macgregor." Set in Benchley's suite at the Royalton.

205 "The Brancusi was dead. . . ."

Manuscript in pencil, 17 pages. Pagination 1–11, 13, 1–3, 1–2. Part of "Garden of Eden" and/or "Sea Novel"?

206 "A broken heart does not come from poverty. . . ."
Typescript, corrected in pencil, one page. Reflections.

207 "The color of a retreat is grey."
Manuscript in pencil, one sheet folded in four. Pagination 1–4.

208 "Coming out the harbour . . ."
Manuscript in pencil, one sentence.

209 "The dark red painted doorways . . ."
Manuscript in pencil, one page. Impressionistic description—of Havana?

210 "Dave O'Neill cut down all the trees. . . ."
[A] Typescript, pencil corrections, one page. "The days on the boat were very long. . . ."
[B] Typescript, corrected, one page. Passage to Europe, 1921.

211 "Do you know a good opening . . . ?"
Typescript, uncorrected, one page. Playing with Marvell's "To His Coy Mistress."

212   "Doc Brown had a thin mouth. . . ."

Pencil, one sentence only.

213   "The fastest moves of all . . ."

Typescript, corrected, two pages. On fighting cocks. Fiction.

214   "The Final Sprint"

Typescript, two pages, corrected. Pagination 1–2. Five sentences only. "This is . . . about a Six Day bicycle race."

215   "The first time I met Ashworth was at the Kavinsky restaurant in Constantinople. . . ."

[A] Manuscript in pencil, four pages. Pagination 1–2, 1–2.

[B] "It was dusty in Constantinople. . . ." Another, very different, draft.

216   Folder of Typescript and Manuscript Fragments

Thirty sheets of miscellaneous manuscript notes, mostly in pencil. On "David Bourne," Evan Shipman, Robert Desnos, "Paris book," drafts of telegrams. On envelope, three notes by EH: "Mss of 1957," "in progress," "some to be reworked, some to be discarded. Just as was beside the typewriter on left on workshelf." "Uncopied starts on stories."

217 "Foreword to Next Book"

Manuscript in ink, corrections, one page. Opens "A good story needs no explanations. . . ."

218 "Fortunately you love your family. . . ."

Manuscript in pencil, one page written on both sides. Sentence drafts.

219 "A French officer running down the street with his pants off is ridiculous says Jane Heep [*sic*]."

Typescript, one page. Mention of Hadley.

220 "The Fugitive"

Manuscript in pencil, one page. Sentence drafts.

221 "Gentlemen etc. etc. etc. Thank you very much for this prize. . . ."

Four penciled pages. Pagination 1–4. Sardonic, unused version of Nobel Acceptance speech.

222 "Girls in Switzerland cannot marry. . . ."

Typescript, two sentences.

223 "got bored last night or maybe . . . just faintly pissed."

Manuscript, one page, dated "24/3/50—0630."

224 "Good News from the Mainland"

Opens "The wind blew out of the South. . . ." Two pages, pencil, heavily revised.

225 "In the night he slept with his pillow doubled over. . . ."

Manuscript in ink, corrected, two pages. Paginated 1–2.

226 "have been wiser not to have tried to do the two things."

Manuscript in pencil, one page. Pagination 7. (Reference to head injury in London, World War II.)

227 "He lived alone in his house with his son. . . ."

Typescript, corrected, two pages. Pagination 1–2. Set in Paris, about Bumby (John Hemingway). Pencil draft mentioning Italy on verso of second page.

228 "How to Review Books"

Typescript, two pages, corrected in type. Complete?

229 "I could not tell him of hemlock needles. . . ."

Manuscript in pencil. One sentence for "Fathers and Sons."

230   "I don't say you will not be a coward. . . ."

Manuscript in pencil, one sentence.

231   " 'I guess so,' she admitted."

Typescript, one page. Pagination 4. Fragment of "The Last Good Country"?

232   " 'I want to stay,' she reached for the pistol."

Manuscript in pencil, four pages. Pagination 27–30. Police in Cuba, man and girl. Part of "The Flower of the Party," published as "Nobody Ever Dies," *Cosmopolitan,* March, 1939.

233   "I wish I had never gone out there. . . ."

Manuscript in pencil, one page.

234   "In Madrid it can be so hot at night. . . ."

Manuscript in pencil, one page.

235   "In the fall people shut . . ."

Manuscript in pencil, one page, written on both sides. Draft for part of "The Three-Day Blow"? Or "Jimmy Breen"?

236 "In the pensione Aguilar . . ."

Manuscript in pencil, two pages. Poetic sketch.

237 "In those days there was the North Prairie. . . ."

Manuscript in pencil, six pages. Pagination 1–6. Snakes in a prairie. Ursula or Madelaine [Hemingway] comes with the protagonist. Part of "The Last Good Country"?

238 "Insert to Book V"

Manuscript in ink, four pages. Pagination 2–4, [ ]. For "Garden of Eden"? On death of a bullfighter named Vicente Girones.

239 "It had been twilight outside. . . ."

Manuscript in pencil, one page. Mention of "Gran Rue de Pera." Constantinople. For "The Snows of Kilimanjaro"?

240 "It seems there is not any sex in this book. . . ."

Manuscript in pencil, two pages. About a small boy called "Jimmy House." Perhaps Jimmy Breen?

241 "It was happy and it was something and we all liked it."

Typescript, two pages. First page on half sheet.

242 "It was time to go to bed. . . ."

Manuscript in pencil, two pages.

243 "I've got to get it over, he said. . . ."

Manuscript in pencil, one page.

244 "I've seen him when we used to row. . . ."

Manuscript in pencil, two pages. Pagination 6, 8 [?]. Ernest as boy in boat, thinking about mother and father.

245 "Last spring Mac and I decided to go to Spain. . . ."

Typescript, four pages, corrected in pencil. McAlmon, Hadley, Mike and Maggie Strater.

246 "Lawrence lived alone comfortably. . . ."

Typescript, two pages. Detailed sketch of "Larry Taine," bookstore proprietor, expatriate, translator, who acts as guide on trip to Chartres.

247 "The Life Work and Evil Fate of Dr. Cadman."
                                        (*unpublished*)

Typescript, five pages. Pagination 1–4, [5]. Assorted drafts under various titles as follows:

[i] "Benchley: The Image and the Man." Typescript, carbon, uncorrected, three pages. Dialogue: Benchley and Abraham Lincoln.

[ii] "Benchley and the Young Lincoln." Typescript, uncorrected, one page. Pagination 2.

[iii] "Benchley: The Image and the Man. The Story Up to This Point." Typescript, two pages.

248 "The lines around the eyes of Anselmo . . ."

Manuscript in pencil, one page, written on both sides. *For Whom the Bell Tolls?*

249 *The Lost Generation A Novel*

"Foreword," three pages in pencil, pagination 1–3, running backward in a notebook. Partly a version of the Stein anecdote on the "lost generation." Conversation over a bottle of wine, in same notebook with draft of "Indian Camp."

250 " 'May is the most beautiful month of the year,' she said."

Typescript, uncorrected, one page.

251 "Mss-Schruns"

Notebook containing the following sketches:

[i] "Boxing is funny that way," eight pages.

[ii] "The Bull Ring," five pages. Opens "We had gone from Switzerland to Rapallo. . . ." Mentions invitation to visit from Pound.

[iii] On verso pages: "Chicuelo—The Phenomenon," nine pages. Pagination 37–45. *Not* the famous bull-fighter.

252 "Nacional II was a bull fighter."

Manuscript in ink, three pages. Unpaginated, written on both sides.

253 "Nick Nerone was an officer. . . ."

Manuscript in pencil, one page, written on both sides. Notes on Paul Dallas Rust, Krebs Friend.

254 "Nick was undressing in the tent."

Manuscript in ink, eight pages. Paginated 1–8. Probable original opening to "Indian Camp."

255 "No Mans Library—Books Not Published by the Three Mountains Press."

Typescript, one page. Two titles only: "Female Virgins and Male Masturbators," and "The Man Who Married a Bum Wife."

256 Notebook labeled "Private"

Contains incomplete sketch in ink, on unruled paper, recto only, ten pages. About girl from Paris, who came to Schruns for a visit. Also computations of expenses and cash on hand, December 1, 1924—December 17, 1924.

257 "Now is the time for all good men to come to the aid of the country."

Typescript, one page. Paginated 52.

258 "Oh Canada"

Typescript, original, two pages. Corrections in type. Opens "The view from the apartment is very fine." On birth of John Hemingway.

259 "Olive oil and leather . . ."

Manuscript in ink, two pages.

260 One sheet paged 14 with line "was killed by an avalanche."

261 Page of dialogue.

Manuscript in ink. Between a night clerk and a taxi driver.

262   Page of dialogue.

Manuscript in ink. Opening in hand of MH, reply by EH.

263   "Paris 1922"

Typescript, two pages, corrected. Six one-sentence prose sketches on Paris. Published in Carlos Baker's *Ernest Hemingway: a Life Story,* pp. 90–91.

264   "In Paris there was a revolution. . . ."

Notebook, blue, stenographic, early winter, 1925. Four-page fragment. Unfinished story. Also a list of letters to write, including a "must write" file; notes on manuscripts sent out and returned. On back cover, list of books taken to Schruns.

265   "Part of Book"

Manuscript in pencil, four pages. Pagination 1–4. Opens "When I would wake up in the morning . . ." On a ship in rough weather. Part of "Along with Youth"?

266   "Paul Dallas Rust was Richard Harding Soper's assistant. . . ."

Manuscript in pencil, one page. On verso: " 'Say Jack,' I said, 'How did you happen to beat Leonard.' " (Anecdote eventually deleted from "Fifty Grand.") (Soper was on *Co-operative Commonwealth* in Chicago, 1920.)

267 Postcard with note by EH, n.d.

"I believe in the historical necessity of the Cuban Revolution and believe in its long range aims. I do not wish to discuss personalities or day to day problems."

268 "Rapallo"

Typescript, one page, pencil corrections. Opens "Cats love the garden. . . ." On Hadley, Ezra, Sweeny (Charles ?), Henry and Maggie Strater.

269 "Simon Green was the only rich Indian."

One typed sentence for "The Petoskey road . . ."

270 "So, I said, what shall I write . . . ?" "About marriage, she said."

Typescript, one page. (". . . the only way that I know to write fast enough so that the machine will drown out the wood scraper is to write in a biblical style. And so it came to pass and so on.")

271 "So Mr. Questioner says . . ."

Typescript, corrected, one page.

272 "Smiths"

Manuscript in ink, one page. One paragraph opening "Kenley Smith was the good looking one. . . ."

273   "Spain"

Manuscript in ink, eleven pages. Pagination 1–3, [1]–3, [blank,] 3, 2–4. EH and Hadley at a cafe before a *corrida.*

274   " 'Splendid'," the Major said. . . ."

Manuscript in pencil, two pages. Pagination 5–6. Dialogue with Sweeny about sending cables.

275   "A Story to Skip. A Badly Organized Story of No Importance"

Typescript, pencil corrections, one page. Title lined out. Opens "And every July they took him out and broke his heart." Set on a train in Spain.

276   "That spring and summer was the time of the great victories. . . ."

Manuscript in pencil, three pages. Pagination 1–3. Possible opening to Chapter II of *A Farewell to Arms.*

277   "There are only a few good trout streams. . . ."

Manuscript in ink, two pages. Trout and bullfighters in Spain.

278   "There is the time when the story is in the mind. . . ."

Manuscript in pencil, one page.

279 "There were two of them by the side of the road. . . ."

Manuscript in pencil, two pages. Florida Keys in a storm. (Part of "Sea Novel"?)

280 "They call it the Machine age. . . ."

Typescript, ten pages of drafts. Sparse corrections in pencil. Opens "Are artists people? If you prick an artist . . ." A self-interview.

281 "This Machine Age"

Typescript, three pages uncorrected. Opens "Is there any machine . . ." Rue des Italiens address.

282 "They left on a Thursday. . . ."

Manuscript in ink, one page. On ocean fishing.

283 *They Never Came Back*

"Outline of 2nd book of short stories" One page on loose notebook cover. List of titles for stories. Book did not take this form.

284 "They say that you can never go back. . . ."

Manuscript in pencil, five pages. Pagination 1–5. On the siege of Madrid.

285 "This was a great place before the war, John. . . ."

Manuscript in pencil, insert four, page six. For "The Flower of the Party"?

286 "Tribal custom the Irish being a savage people . . ."

Typescript, one page, uncorrected.

287 "Twice in the night he got up from his bed. . . ."

Manuscript in pencil, two pages. Michigan in dreams.

288 Unidentified page of a Nick Adams story: "insert nine" to page 21.

289 ". . . the war monument. There were motor cars. . . ."

Manuscript in ink, two pages. Pagination 3–4. Set in Genoa.

290 ". . . what is it like when he's gone."

Manuscript in pencil, one page. Pagination 442. (End of *To Have and Have Not?*)

291 "What professional boxers fight for . . ."

Typescript, three pages. Pagination [ ], 4–5. Mentions Lardner, Pegler, Siki. Set in Toronto?

292   "The way fish die is most instructive. . . ."

Manuscript in ink, two pages. Pagination 10–12.

293   "We lay at Sou'west Key that night. . . ."

Manuscript in pencil, one page. Part of "After the Storm."

294   "We never caught them as big after the war. . . ."

Manuscript in pencil, four pages. Pagination 1–4. Autobiographical. About learning to write in Upper Michigan.

295   "We used to quarrel before attacks. . . ."

Manuscript in pencil, four pages. Pagination 1–4. Dialogue with girl called Rabbit, mention of Gaylord's. Draft for part of *For Whom the Bell Tolls?*

296   "We were riding out. . . ."

Typescript, original, one and one-half pages. "Wops," Arnstein, race track.

297   "When a man from up North marries a Key West girl . . ."

Manuscript in pencil, four pages. Pagination 1–4. On employment in Key West.

298   "The wind died in the night. . . ."

Two pages, pencil. On a boat in a lagoon, sleeping wife.

299   "The wind woke us in the night. . . ."

Typescript, one page. Tropic setting.

300   [*Winner Take Nothing*]

Manuscript, one page. Draft for epigraph to the collection of stories.

301   "You could not be one Marion said."

Manuscript in pencil. A dialogue about bullfighting.

302   "You love god like that?"

Manuscript in pencil, three pages. Pagination 168–70. Dialogue from *A Farewell to Arms?*

303   "You ought to get to Cuba by April."

Typescript, one page. Pagination 23. "Sea Novel" page. T. Hudson and the Baron in Paris.

LETTERS

304 Letters by EH

[A] 12 folders containing originals, carbons and drafts, some not mailed. Earliest dated July 15, 1915, Walloon Lake, Michigan. Latest dated 1958.

[B] In shopping bag, many originals, photocopies, typed copies, to Harvey Breit, Hadley Hemingway, C. T. Lanham, Bernard Berenson, William Smith, etc.

[C] Also two reels, unidentified microfilm, labeled V.D.-S. (Valery Danby-Smith)

[D] Folders of letters by EH, MH, T. J. Welsh, 1942–43.

305 Letters to EH

[A] Seven folders from family and friends.

[B] Three folders from Curtis Brown.

[C] Five folders from Scribners.

[D] One folder from INS.

[E] Fourteen folders from Toronto *Star*.

[F] Four folders concerning contributions to magazines and anthologies.

[G] Four folders from Italy, 1918–19, by Agnes von Kurowsky, Elsie MacDonald, and others.

[H] Letter from F. Scott Fitzgerald to "Dear Ernest," unsigned, in pencil, n.d., n.p. Ten pages, written on one side only. Pagination 1–10. Much interlinear and marginal correction, many deletions. Inserted in Book III of *Fiesta*. Critique of final typescript of *The Sun Also Rises*.

[I] Letter from Larry Gains: June 19, 1824, two pages.

[J] Letter from Larry Gains, June 25[?], 1925, two pages in ink with envelope marked "answered June 21[?]." Possible models for letter from Negro fighter in *Fiesta*. Gains' letters in *Fiesta* notebooks.

MISCELLANEOUS

306   Five albums on EH, kept by Grace Hall Hemingway from 1899 through graduation from high school, June, 1917.

307   Daybook, 1924, and Diary, 1924.

Sketches, fragments of sentences, scattered entries, mostly on expenses.

308   "Joke is Warlike"

Clipping dated June 23, 1917, from unidentified newspaper. Concerns an attack on EH and some friends as a joke which ended in a brawl. EH lists the injuries and injured on the clipping.

309   "Suggestions Hotch omit Death in the After-noon . . . ?"

Manuscript in pencil, four passages.

310   Folder containing World War I data and photocopy of EH will, dated Sept., 1955. Contains C. E. Hemingway's letters from American Red Cross, May 20, 1918, July 20, 1918, and a telegram, August 13, 1918.

311   Form for Oak Park War Memorial filled out by EH, n.d. "Wounded July 8, 1918—Fossalta di Piave." (Cf. poem, "Killed," item 152.) "Piave Major defensive June 15—July 8, 1918." "Monte Grappa Offensive Oct 26—Nov 2 Vittoria Veneto." Related letters from Donald L. Campbell and T. D. Brumback, with clipping from N.Y. *Telegram* of July 17, 1918: "Newspaper Man Survives 200 Battle Wounds."

312   Commission of American Red Cross, Report of the Department of Military Affairs, Rome, 1918, covering period January to July, 1918. On page 15 is list of lieutenants in charge of canteens. EH listed as "E. K. Hemingway."

313   Journal of Expenses, April, 1922, Paris. Also notes on correspondence, appointments, meals. Some notes on events in Genoa.

314   In EH hand: "45 chest   39 waist   17½ neck."

315   Notebook, one and one-fourth pages of penciled notes.

316 Notebook listing contents of *Three Stories and Ten Poems*. Also fragments on Spain, note on anarchy there.

317 Notebook with three items in ink on one page relating to a circus, a man returning to Paris from the States, and a lottery. Also a card and signature.

318 Clipping book for *The Torrents of Spring* and *The Sun Also Rises*.

319 Clipping book for "Fifty Grand."

320 Clipping books on African crashes, one bound in zebra, the other in antelope.

321 Seven folders of review clippings, 1923–29.

322 Single folder containing postcard from EH to Gerald and Sara Murphy, note by EH to write Maxwell Perkins, etc.

323 Book, black buckram, with "2" written on spine, all pages blank but first six. Unpaginated. On frontispiece in pen: "Ernest Hemingway March 6, 1926, Note Book." KW

[A] Page one reads "Titles For the Stories—A New Slain Knight" followed by "I must finish The Sun Also Rises and then want to write short stories for four to five months—" First page of text begins "When I feel low I like to think about death and the various ways of dying . . ." (mostly suicidal).

[B] "A New Slain Knight," two pages. Unpaginated. Begins "I will write a picaresque novel for America. It will be about Red Ryan. . . ." Ends: "(This is horseshit)" Then: "Most of what I write is horseshit." Property of Betty Bruce.

324 Folder containing EH notes in Spanish and English on bullfighters and cost of bullfighting, prizefighters, difficulty of getting stories published, topics for stories to write, cancelled checks, shopping lists, liquor and fishing expenses, fish caught, assignment sheet for reporters, including EH, on *Kansas City Star* for January 3, 1918, and piece of thick cardboard with practice titles —e.g., "The Manner of the Accident"—for "The Short Happy Life of Francis Macomber." KW

COPIES OF BOOKS
AND MAGAZINES

325 Ernest Hemingway, *Three Stories and Ten Poems* (Dijon, 1923).

In original unbroken wrapper.

326 Ernest Hemingway, *in our time* (Paris, 1924).

Copy presented to Jack Cowles by "Hank S." in N.Y.C., 1924. Later presented by Cowles to EH, February 14, 1926.

327 Ernest Hemingway, *Today is Friday* (Englewood, N.J., 1926).

328 Ford Madox Ford, *No More Parades*.

Typescript, 294 pages, dated "Paris 31/10/24, Guermantes 25/4/25." In binder with Ford's address. Manuscript heavily corrected, with several full-page inserts in Ford's hand. D. Harvey's Ford bibliography locates no manuscript or typescript for this book.

329   James Joyce, *Ulysses* (Paris, 1922).

Unbound, stamped "Press Copy." Signed in red pencil, "Ernest M. Hemingway."

330   Ezra Pound, *XVI Cantos* (Paris, 1924).

Number 10 of 90. "Printed for Ernest Hemingway."

331   Gertrude Stein, *Portrait of Mabel Dodge* (Florence, 1913[?]).

Presentation copy: "To the Hemingways with much affection. Gertrude Stein."

332   Copies of magazines in which EH contributions appeared: *Querschnitt, Little Review, This Quarter, Scribner's, Double-Dealer, Poetry* (EH contributions cut out). Also newspaper: *Frankfurter Zeitung,* "Das Ende von Etwas," and other stories.

INDEX

Note: the numbers (and letters) after each entry in this index refer *not* to page numbers but to the inventory identification numbers.